D0105683

FOCUS

FOCUS

The Cry for Bread

By ANNA J. LINDGREN

MOODY PRESS

CHICAGO

INTRODUCTION

Mᴇʟʟᴏᴡᴇᴅ by a generation of rest from public view, *Esther Winge* reappears on the literary scene in contemporary garb, responding to the curtain call of Space-Age personalities and pressures.

Previously *Esther Winge* spoke only Swedish when published in Stockholm in the early thirties, a Swedish best seller. Like a church bell pealing on a crisp Swedish winter morning, *Esther Winge* sounded clearly the tones of a restless humanity — Russian-born revolutionaries, anti-Semites, union organizers and the mechanical grinding of "cog-thinkers."

One generation later in *Focus*, Esther Winge speaks again — in English to a world still perplexed by the "cry of terror," the eternal cry for bread. This cry is as real in the Space Age with its eastern European satellites as it was thirty years earlier in the twentieth century when eastern European immigrants were free to swarm into America.

The cry for bread is still heard today over the clanging of shuttles and the whirring of wheels in some places. The cry yet resounds in the animated, midnight group discussions of dissatisfied immigrants. The need for a focus on life is as great today as it was a generation ago. Missiles, satellites and Telstars have not beamed new light into the shadows of man's dilemma.

From all points of the compass comes the unrelenting wail of the undernourished, augumented by the crescendo of toddlers' feet which confirms the population explosion. From the womb of colonialism have been born scores of infant nations in the post-World-War-II era. Their cry for bread is punctuated by the collective shrieks of economic hunger pangs from suckling ethnic groups. To these and all who hunger in the inner man and who turn their eyes in fear and perplexity to the man-made objects in space, Esther Winge articulates hope.

Focus centers on the individual, without whom nations would not exist. Esther Winge, youthful and ambitious, intellectual and idealistic, sensitive — "almost fragile" — struggles intensively with the focus on herself in the searchings of her soul for the rationale of living — to see, and in seeing, to find the True Bread that never perishes, but always nourishes, and "the peace that passes understanding."

A personal diary portraying the hate of racism, the tensions of unionism, the gnawing dissatisfaction of skepticism, the insatiable yearning to love and be loved, here the tangled strands of frustration and confusion of the inquiring mind and the seeking heart are woven into the warp and woof of a meaningful pattern for living. The diary brings into view the life which has found the answer to the cry for bread for the labor organizer and social worker, the capitalist and the agnostic — and all who seek.

That is a satisfaction which comes only from seeing — in focus!

The quest for a perspective on reality marks the soul's search for the satisfying life. The life which asks for no more bread has focused on the True Bread — and is satisfied. The mind at ease is the soul at peace. The struggle for satisfaction which comes with understanding terminates with the focus on the whole of life — the soul at rest in the fact of God. This is the God who reveals Himself and gives Himself to and for man the sinner — hungry and lost.

This fact is a revolution, an internal revolution first — for each of us. It becomes a point of reference which quells the conflict of doubt and despair in the agnostic, the rebellion

6

in the labor organizer, the intrigue of the irascible capitalist. It unites the souls of all men through a regenerating experience of new eyes — that focus!

Esther Winge struggles with the dissatisfaction of the searching soul and speaks to the unsatisfaction of the materialism of the satellite-missile era.

Author Anna Lindgren, whose previous volumes* have shown her to be acquainted with the soul of man, penetrates the depths of the human personality, uncovers the longings of the heart and succinctly depicts the crisis of faith which ultimately grips reality.

There is that called faith which is only a veneer for undefined feelings; *Focus* centers on the struggle without faith and breaks through into the rest of faith, the faith that sees with clarity and satisfies the inner hunger.

> H. Wilbert Norton
> President, Trinity College and
> Trinity Theological Seminary

---

*With Him; In His Presence; Afterglow; Charlotte A. Cary, Gentlewoman of God.

Chicago, September 16, 1913

Whenever I sit by my machine I have the oddest sensation of being cut off from organic life. I seem to be turned into a cog in a gigantic, pounding, roaring, world-encircling system of big and little wheels, screws and levers, constantly gripped by other cogs, driven by them and driving them, without thought, volition or aim, just whirling, clanging, rushing-round-round-round.

So strong is this impression that I rarely feel tired when working. My foot seems welded to its treadle, my knee frozen in its bent position, and my hands are working automatically. Not until the motor stops with a convulsive jerk and the sudden silence brings a dulling dizziness, as if the atmospheric pressure had suddenly ceased, do I drop from weariness. Even a laugh, rebounding in a thousand echoes in this empty, uncanny silence, can cause tears to flow down my cheeks, and I have to bite my lips to keep from sobbing.

It was particularly the first days that this happened. Gradually the nervous tension and my reaction to it became a habit, a fact to take into account. My rational self, set aside when I became an automaton during working hours and after work a part of me again, becomes more watchful and cautious with each passing day. This splitting of my personality frightens me at times. I feel that I am always watched, pursued, and never alone. But isn't it also the only escape from overstrain and desperate weariness? I can't ever risk being as tired as I was my first day in the factory. That can happen only the first time. No one can endure a repetition. Rather this duality then. It has become such a habit with me to cut off all association of ideas connected with that memory that I seldom think of it. Only occasionally, in unguarded moments, can I catch swift glimpses from that day as one might, in looking through the window of a moving train, catch reflections of the landscape on the opposite side.

Sometimes, in these fleeting pictures, I can see myself as an infinitesimal speck in a dark, surging maelstrom of humanity pouring out from the yawning exits of factories and shops, swelling like a tidal wave, then gradually dissipating, swallowed up by shadowy slums or carried off by speeding streetcars. Sometimes, with a shudder, I can hear the cry of terror that escaped my lips the first time I was carried on the crest of the wave across a thoroughfare, heard the thundering roar of the elevated train over my head, and saw the lightning-like, blue-green flares from the electric network of the streetcars. But most frequently I see the picture I try the hardest to forget—myself stumbling through dark alleys and deserted streets, driven by a nameless despair, not daring to go home for fear I might meet someone that would know me and see my anguish. Exhausted, I finally sank down on a pile of lumber behind a fence and burst into tears, the uncontrolled, hopeless weeping of a child, sobbing out a single word—*mother—mother—mother—*

It still is not clear to me how I got home that night, but in the gray dawn of the next morning I woke up, stiff with cold, slumped over the table.

Two years have passed since then. Day after day I have taken my place in the line, awaiting my turn to be packed into the iron cage of the elevator, dumped on the tenth floor, becoming a cog, gripped by other cogs, driven by them and driving them without thought, volition or aim, just whirling, clanging, rushing—round—round—round—

My mechanical nature quickly developed. It soon found itself in the world system of cogs. It began to dream cog-dreams and think cog-thoughts; began to philosophize over the construction and meaning of so gigantic an organism; began to distinguish voices and words in its roaring, surging clatter.

Thus, like the enchanted prince of the fairy tale, we live our dual existence, deep within us nourishing a vague hope that one day the miracle will take place, the formula be found, the magic word be spoken that will forever liberate the spirit of man from the shackles of materialism.

WE! That is the great gladness and the great torment. In the heat of the struggle the thought lifts and thrills me that I am a part of the WHOLE—that my happiness is dependent on the happiness of others. It gives meaning and greatness to my little life. It gives me courage and responsibility. It causes my own feeling of aloneness to be submerged in a flood of compassion for the deep loneliness that stares out of a million tired eyes and care-lined faces on the streets of the big city. I never need to look at my own threadbare coat to feed my indignation on the inequalities of our economic system. What is the individual in comparison to the race? My life is but a drop, a speck of dust. But let the drop fall into the flood that one day shall break down the sluice gates of selfishness. Let the speck of dust be trampled on the highway of Freedom and Truth!

September 17

RETURNED today to the factory. Maria was there, the Maria Polovsky of last year, only more intense. The big, dark-brown eyes seem bigger, the olive skin darker, the

11

black hair wavier, the whole personality more vivid. In this she is an exception. Ever since childhood days I have found disappointment in seeing someone again after a prolonged absence. Though the memory had grown, the reality remained unchanged. But Maria is not a disappointment. When she caught sight of me, she came running with open arms and tear-wet cheeks. "Esther Winge, oh, Esther Winge, to see you again!" And we can talk together! True, our language is still broken, and sometimes we have to search desperately for words. But even if we do not always find the right one, we usually find some that sympathetic understanding can interpret, and that was seldom the case last year. What a pity that two young, intelligent people, drawn to each other in instantaneous liking, should have no medium for exchange of thought! Truly "the confusion of tongues" was a curse.

There is something entirely new about Maria. The dark eyes still wear the crepe of a haunting sadness, but somehow it only enhances this newness as sunlight, flickering through the dense shadow of a forest, may seem brighter, mirrored in the dusky depth of a pool. Who is she? What mysterious feeling of kinship draws me to this young Jewess from Russia? It goes deeper than a mere national instinct, which often leads to recognition and approach amidst hundreds of strangers. I glance over to the next machine where she sits stooped over her work, and a great gladness wells up within me because she is there. She is like an adventure waiting to be lived.

The factory is the same. The Slavonian immigrants are in the majority—as usual. I sit close to them, and their—to me—unintelligible babble reaches me through the clattering roar as a haunting melody for which I must find words. The first-generation Americans are also there, girls with painted, powdered faces and jaunty airs. I have very little in common with them. I can't quite forgive them for disappointing me so sorely. That's my colossal stupidity. They have no inkling that Esther Winge is taking them to task for departing from ideals they never had. Why should not my love embrace them with the same warm sympathy that draws me to their parents, the immigrants? A commendable tolerance that allows itself to be duped by a little cheap elegance, borne with youthful aplomb! Reluctantly I approve of a nature fundamentally different from my own, unless I can play the role of benefactress.

September 18

I NEVER get tired of listening to Maria. She possesses the peculiar gift of the Jewish race to be able to speak without words, with a play of the features, a gesture of the hand, a shrug of the shoulder, a sideways glance. She can relate an event, tell a life story with such moving realism that it seems that you were there, that the experience was yours. The suffering of another painfully carves its runes in your own soul, and the burdens of another press you to the ground.

Her voice is low and monotonous, without modulation, but it holds you spellbound. Her long, slender, expressive hands are forever in motion, as if playing an accompaniment. All her movements are soft, measured, full of pathos.

Through our conversations she is opening to me a world of suffering I never knew existed. The old legend about the wandering Jew comes back with renewed emphasis and meaning. Maria herself has suffered terribly. Last spring she worked in the factory as long as there was any work to be had. Sometimes she barely made enough for food and lodging. Bitterly hopeless it seemed, this slavery for a mere existence. So this, then, was the reward for years of study, the fulfillment of youthful dreams, the penalty for revolutionary ideas and plans for world betterment! Ha—ha, a world to live in! In all of Russia could there have been a class of girls with a more glowing patriotism or a greater hunger for righteousness? In all the world could there have been a group of students more in earnest about social wrongs or more willing to give their lives for their nation than these girls in a half-barbaric land?

Sarah Spiowaky, the genius of the class, was married to the young, promising sculptor Ivanovich, who at the time of his first exhibition in Paris was arrested as a revolutionary and was in prison the first year of their married life. Scarcely had he been released before he was ordered out to three years of military service. And Sarah, without money, without home, taken in by a poor, old relative out of charity, is now awaiting her baby.

Thus revolutionaries are born in Russia.

And there was Anna Jutan, the unyielding idealist, who never could compromise or bargain. Life had no use for her. She realized it—and went. Ah, Maria can't think of her without remorse. When Anna had returned from France after having completed language studies, eager to find her place and begin to realize her ideals, she found that every door was closed to her because her father was a Jew. She wrote to Maria asking for a ticket to America. But Maria herself had been struggling against sheer poverty, enduring cold and hunger to save pennies for postage home, and in despair she blurted out the truth about "the promised land," as it appeared to her. The next letter from home told of Anna's suicide.

And so they had gone, one after the other, exiled, beaten, persecuted, more familiar with suffering than with anything else.

"I can't understand," I said, "how a race without a country, dispersed over all the world, have been able to preserve their identity through thousands of years."

"For a long time," Maria answered, "I thought that hate separated my people from all other peoples of the world. When I saw our homes devastated, our young men exiled, our young women ravished and trampled on, my hate grew until it filled my soul, blinding, consuming. I thought it holy, flowing from the same wellspring as the hatred of Yahwe, the God of our fathers. I wanted to strike back, smite down, take revenge. I was very young then. A passion as intense as my hatred is doomed to be consumed by its own flame. In its place came pride, the pride that is characteristic of our race and that you Christians have mistaken for cowardliness. I have seen our venerable patriarchs, silently bow under the smarting blows from the Cossacks' whips and robbed of the fruits of a lifelong toil without protest begin anew a dogged fight against poverty and contempt. True, their protests would have been of no avail. But only great, farseeing souls can suffer in silence.

"Characteristically, nominal Christendom is blinded to the fact that the tables have been turned. The race, of whom the Nazarene said, 'Forgive them, for they know not what they do,' has now taken His place, while His so-called followers are the executors. I know what is in your mind just now. You see before you the typical Jew, as he is found in the big industrial centers—the shyster, the loan shark, the sweatshop driver, the egotistical, ruthless businessman, the type with the long nose and the grasping hand, Shakespeare's Shylock. Is he an enigma? Is it surprising that some were not big enough for the big horizons? Do you wonder that they chose to avenge themselves for personal and national injustices in the only way open to them? I am not defending the type, but I find it understandable.

15

"Enter the home of the loan shark, and you will see him as he is, without his mask. In the husband and father you will find not the characteristics you have assigned to the typical Jew but rather a fidelity and love that has kept our race sound and strong through the millenniums, while other nations have degenerated and declined. Our racial solidarity and isolation are the result of inviolate loyalty to inherited laws."

"Your laws are all of a religious nature?"

"I would turn it around and say that our laws are our religion, and our religion is inseparable from life itself. We do not recognize your dualism of religion and society. Religion to us is not something apart from our everyday living, something you can take or leave. It is our way of life. Since time began religion has set men apart and built boundaries around them, and the line of demarcation has ever been directly related to the believer's loyalty to his creed. With us this loyalty is so great that only occasionally does an individual break with tradition and depart from the faith of his fathers."

"Would you say this loyalty is as pronounced in the new generation?"

"I see what you mean. No, we of the younger generation do not have faith, but we are faithful. I do not actually know any young people who 'believe' in our sacred writings, but we believe in the commandment, 'Honor thy father and thy mother.'"

It was during the lunch hour this conversation took place. And while I listened, I made a discovery that filled me with wonder. It seems to me that heart and mind were completely absorbed in the story Maria told, and yet my immediate surroundings made an indelible impression. I can close my eyes now and see every detail in the room. It was as if I had seen it for the first time, as if I had suddenly

16

awakened from deep sleep and found myself in a strange place. Day after day I have seen the women getting together with their sandwiches and teapots, forming the same cliques, but today I saw them in a new light. I saw why the coteries existed, saw the impulse behind them. I saw each individual in each group, and how each one was a separate world. I saw the long tables stretching from wall to wall, loaded down with material, great heaps of hats in the process of making, some without shape as yet, only splashes of gaudy colors, others half finished. I saw the floor littered with scraps and rubbish and was conscious of the strong smell of wet varnish from newly blocked hats. The long rows of windows on the two outside walls, completely covered with soot and dust, were opened from the top, making the dim contours of the city below seem more misty gray than ever. Tattered bits of window shades flapped in the lazy breeze. The atmosphere was oppressively heavy. Still, I never gave a conscious thought to all this. My mind was captivated by her story and at the same time puzzled over this awareness of the surroundings.

"What are you thinking about?" asked Maria.

"I am wondering what you would do if you had to choose between your parents' wishes and the demands of your heart."

"I could never love a Christian."

"You don't mean that!"

"With all my soul. I promised my mother, on my fifteenth birthday, that I would never marry a Christian. That promise was not difficult to give and has never been difficult to keep. The butchering of the Jews in 1907 gave me the baptism of blood that for all time will bind me to my people. No love is great enough to fully understand the supersensitivity that is our heritage from centuries of suffering, and never could my soul find rest in another soul that had not been wounded and had not nearly bled to death through this sensitivity."

"I can readily understand such an attitude in Russia, but—"

"Ha-ha-ha—!" It was a laugh that hurt. A laugh that sobbed. "The other day my friend Vera and her husband went around looking for an apartment. They returned toward evening more tired than I have ever seen them. No one takes them to be Jews. They are both blond and Vera, particularly, has a very winning personality. They found an apartment they liked and decided on. Everything seemed settled, when the landlord asked their nationality. 'Jews? Very sorry. That changes everything. I would lose all my tenants if it were known I have taken in Jews. Sorry.' He was a Swede but no exception. They got the same answer over and over again. And here you have another answer to your question as to how we have kept our identity. You Christians have helped us."

"But why?"

Maria lifted her shoulders in a characteristic shrug that said so unmistakably, "Don't ask me!"

After a brief silence she said in a changed, thoughtful voice, "It isn't half so much a question of principle as of economy. People are not so bad, they are driven by the instinct of self-preservation—necessity. Our national recovery will probably be a part of—" Her last words were drowned in the din of a hundred machines the moment the power was on. Here time was money in the full sense of the word, and no one was inclined to waste much of that commodity, Maria and I not excepted. Dozens after dozens of hats grew as if by magic, and the foreman had never seemed quicker to supply us with material. All afternoon not a word was spoken.

September 19

ARE SOME born doers and others dreamers? Has the dreamer a mission to fulfill, or is he one of nature's failures?

September 25

Is MAN the only form of life through which the river of life was permitted to flow, unshackled and free, to find ever widening channels? If so, it can only be true in a general and limited sense. Many, many persons are barriers and blind alleys. Are they at fault? Is matter responsible to life for following its inherent laws? Can a man choose his lifework and miss his calling? If he consciously submits himself, lives in harmony with the laws of nature and uses them, is it not because in him life has triumphed? On the other hand, if he bends as a slave, is it not because in him brute matter predominated? Who is to blame?

But if my conscious being refuses to surrender itself to the upward surge, I am a criminal, a barrier to life. There is something in the talk about my body as the temple of the "Holy Spirit!"

Monday night

> Are not hands outreaching,
> And kindred spirits greeting,
> Amongst those encountered
> In hate and strife?
>
> (Stjerne)

LAST SATURDAY evening I went home with Maria from the factory. She is Vera Dubow's star boarder. They invited me to remain over the weekend.

A group of young, radical, Russian Jews gather every Saturday night in Nathan's and Vera's home to discuss social and literary questions. It is a free, informal gathering where anyone is welcome who has an independent opinion and dares to express it. At first the conversation was carried on in Russian. Although I did not understand it, I felt strangely moved. As with Maria, it isn't so much the words—or the subject—that grip as the intensity and earnestness. It seemed to me that I could breathe freely there. We have much in common. They are skeptics and seekers after truth. They are strangers in a foreign land—like myself. They greet me with a warmth and confidence that thrills me. Their esteem is such that it sets me apart as something special, above the average. There is no rest in their company, but a bugle call to battle, the stirring of new thoughts, the pressing on toward new goals.

Several came before supper. Around eight o'clock every seat was occupied in the living room. Some of the group sat on the arms of sofa and chairs, others on the floor. It was Nathan himself who suggested a topic for the evening's discussion by asking if they had all seen the latest *Daily News*. Several said they hadn't, so he unfolded and held up the front page for all to see. It was dominated by a single figure—a giant, and bore the caption, "The Sphinx of the New World." Under the illustration there was a long poem—at least it looked like one from the arrangement of the lines, and although it had no rhymes, it certainly had cadence and pathos.

Nathan read, "With chin resting in his hand, and his brooding, introspective eyes looking out over towering skyscrapers and soot-belching smoke stacks toward the dim, faraway horizon, sits a figure, whose gigantic proportions seem to darken the sun and cast a shadow over the Statue of Liberty. His lips are moving, as if he were talking to himself; but the night is still, and the world holds its breath to listen —

I am the Immigrant.
Since the morning of creation
My never resting feet
Have blazed new trails around the world.
My restless ship has sailed on every sea.
My wanderlust was born out of a desire
For greater freedom and better wages
For the sweat of my brow.
I looked to the United States of America
With eyes kindled with ambition
And heart aflame with new hope.

I have borne my burdens
As America's man of all labor.
I perform eighty-five percent of all labor
In the slaughtering and meat-packing industries;
I perform seven tenths of all labor in the mines.
I perform seventy-eight percent of all the labor
In the cotton mills.
I make nineteen twentieths of all clothing.
I make more more than half of all shoes,
Four fifths of all furniture.
I prepare four fifths of all leather,
I make half of all gloves.
I refine nineteen twentieths of all sugar.
I manufacture half of all tobacco and cigarettes.
And still I am America's great problem.
When I give my blood on the altar of your labor
And lay down my life as burnt offering
To your labor god,
Men pay no more attention than when a sparrow falls.
But my muscles are woven into the texture
Of your national existence.
My children shall be your children,
And your land shall be mine;
For my sweat and my blood are the cement
In the foundation for tomorrow's America.

> If I can be fused into your social order,
> Then the melting pot has stood its test."

It was very still in the room a few moments after Nathan had finished the reading. Then the storm broke. Everyone seemed to have an opinion ready about America's great problem. I wondered what they were saying. A people as isolated as they, and with so intense a racial consciousness, could hardly have come to these shores with any dreams of "melting into the foundation of tomorrow's America." The knowledge I had gained about them threw a new light on America's immigrant problem. I wondered if they could see themselves as a part of this problem. Possibly I have been born with a deep national instinct and a built-in sounding board for patriotism? I don't know, but I could feel my heart expanding for this great, overgrown, gaudy, and noisy land that hitherto had seemed such a riddle.

Suddenly I was interrupted in my musings by Maria, who slipped down beside me and said, "Poor you, who must listen to all this babble and not understand a word!"

"Perhaps I have understood a great deal, even if I couldn't understand the words."

Nathan too turned to me with an apology for their thoughtlessness and asked what my opinion was about the national future of America and especially its immigrant problem.

Conversation died down, and all eyes turned my way. My opinion was far from "ready." When I began speaking, I wasn't at all sure what I would say, but because I sensed their regard, I was able to think aloud. What I said, briefly, haltingly, was this:

"When I landed in America, two years ago, it was Sweden's emigration problem that dominated my thinking. I wanted to know what lay underneath this ever flowing stream of Sweden's youth to the land in the West, and America interested me only as it was related to this problem. Before long, however, I realized how almost impossible it was to make an unbiased appraisal of anything in the chaotic whirlpool of human life America seemed to me during those first few months.

"First of all, I was shocked over its unscrupulous fight for gold. It seemed to me that everything bore the imprint of this strife and that no other values than the dollar were recognized. The sensational, gaudy display in the drugstores of patent medicines and cosmetics and whatnot awakened in me a distrust of medical science, accustomed as I was to the dignified exclusiveness of the Swedish *apotek*. The loud and garish advertising of the theaters struck me as a desecration of the arts, and the clatter of coins during religious services, together with the signboards and agitation of the churches, seemed like blasphemy. The absence of idealism in the labor unions was, however, my greatest disappointment next to the Swedish-American. My first contact with him was a terrible shock. In his speech as well as his ideas he seemed like a traitor to his native land. The young laborer I had seen at home as a torchbearer for democracy and whose emigration I had looked upon as an irreparable loss to our society, I met here as a worldly-wise, complacent family man, whose whole ambition was to attain economic security and give his children a practical education. In him I saw, clearer than in anything else, the imprint of Mammon.

"If America's social, religious, and commercial life seemed strange and puzzling, these impressions were greatly strengthened by what I saw of American politics. It seemed impossible to have confidence in a constitution that would permit a private bargaining with national values. Positions of political and social leadership were often reached by the man with the greatest financial pull, rather than by the one personally best qualified. The multiplied elections also added to the confusion and greatly hampered an objective, over-all view. To the eyes of the newcomer, the whole drama seemed like a game of chance with personal gain as the primary factor and with personal responsibility nowhere in evidence."

(In relating this long speech I really should not put it in quotation marks, for I can't recall exactly the words I used, only the drifts of my thoughts. Furthermore, I can't claim originality, since I have been devouring books and articles on immigration, and my thinking has been colored by views and ideas that seemed reasonable. Especially do I owe much to Professor Haskin, whose deep sympathy, understanding, and wealth of factual knowledge have influenced me greatly.)

"In my study of the problem from the viewpoint of the immigrant I saw the difference between the so-called old and new immigrants. The 'old' came from northwestern Europe, from probably poor but good homes and a well-organized society. They have not only self-respect but also a more or less pronounced social consciousness. They are thrown into a wild struggle for existence. It is difficult for them to retain their self-respect when the word 'foreigner' is sneeringly thrown in their faces on every hand. Even their growing children are ashamed of their broken language and of their own foreign descent. If they succeed to better themselves by dint of brain or brawn or a dogged persistence, they are immediately 'Americans' and do not like to be reminded that they were once aliens.

"It has been said that the Scandinavians provide the best material for citizenship, because of them there is no second generation, since their children become thoroughly Americans. My reaction to such a statement is one of pain.

24

I am Swedish, as you are Jews. Being Swedish does not—
to me—mean wearing a garment that can be taken off as
you please. Should I renounce my citizenship in my father-
land and exchange the Golden Cross for the Star-Spangled
Banner, this act could only be an outward form. I would
ever be true to my adopted land, but deep down in my
inmost soul I would know that I am a stranger. My soul is
Swedish to its color, and that color is at least as 'fast' as the
complexion of the African black. And still they say that
the characteristic of the Swede is an unusual capacity for
assimilation. But I suppose some are born with a stronger
national consciousness than others. Undoubtedly the poets
I have ever loved have influenced my thinking. But it's not
only people and conditions that have made me what I am.
It is, to speak with Heidenstam, the stones, the very ground
on which I played in childhood, and the echoes I heard in
the woods.

"According to Haskin, it is not the so-called 'old immigrant' from northwestern Europe that calls forth our deepest
sympathies, even if he, in exchange for better economic
conditions, must pay a high price in spiritual values, but
the 'new immigrant' from southeastern Europe. Statistics
tell us that three fourths of all immigrants come from
countries where public education is unheard of, where
popular participation in the affairs of the government is
undreamed of, where dire poverty is the rule. Two thirds
of this 'new' immigration comes from the rural village and
is dumped out upon big industrial centers. Vice surrounds
these centers and thrives upon the 'new' immigration, which
feels all of the worst effects of the American civilization and
none of its best.

"Follow one of these immigrants. He comes from a rural
village where he worked on the farms and in the vineyards,
or herded sheep. Landing in a big city, he is immediately

beset by those who would exploit him. Off he goes to some industrial center where he must live in places scarcely fit for human habitation, crowded with a dozen others in a shack scarcely big enough for two. The work he finds is either filthy or dangerous. He goes into the coal mine, into the fertilizer factory, into the wood-working plant, into the slaughterhouse—everywhere that there is work too disagreeable or dangerous for the native American workingman. With few women among them to cast a refining influence over them, they spend their time between working and drinking, as a rule, saving what they can with the day in view when they can return to their native land. In the vast majority of cases their condition, for the time being, is worse in America than it was in their native lands. But they sacrifice themselves today in America in order that tomorrow at home they may live in comfort. If they lived according to American standards, their wages would barely suffice to keep them going. But they will half starve themselves and live in the worst of surroundings for the sake of going back home some day.

"Tonight I have seen the land of the immigrant from a new point of view for me—America's. Perhaps what Nathan read to us from the daily paper opened my eyes. I don't know what you have said. Possibly I have repeated your words, but what I now am going to say may not meet with your approval. The right I claim for myself to retain my national distinction I also ought to grant to America, wouldn't you agree?"

"But America has no national distinction. It is a composite of all nations, and its task is to let every nationality within its borders retain its distinction, develop into its highest self."

The answer came with lightning-like speed from one of the young men and gave me a clue to what they might previously have said. I replied, "It might be true that the soul of America has not yet suffered the birthpangs of a deep self-consciousness. In spite of its noisy patriotism, it is still a child. But it is also true that a type is developing and clearly discernible that we call *The American.* He can boast of few traditions, but he is proud of those that are his own. That type, as it emerges in its best representatives, is so full of youthful power and realistic idealism that the world cannot afford to do without it."

"How can you speak of a clearly discernible type from a land that annually receives a million aliens?"

"Aliens, to be sure, in speech, customs and ideals but, related in their hunger for happiness, freedom and ambition, they intensify rather than weaken the type. There is something in the lines we read about 'The Melting Pot.' The tiny mountain stream, tumbling over rocks, cascading over steep inclines on its hurried journey to the valley, is easily controlled, but after it has grown into a mighty river, and the river has made its bed to the sea, floods may overrun its banks, but not change its course. I believe America has found its floodbed, and that its greatest task today is to guide into proper channels and surround with desirable influences this turbulent flow of strangers to its shores.

"Transformed into good American citizens, fused into the national life in the melting pot of Americanization, they can be made to constitute a great political and economic asset. On the other hand, left to form themselves into colonies which come into contact only with the worst element of the native population, removed from the better influences of America's national life, never learning its language, never adopting its customs, never sensing its ideals, and never catching the spirit of its civilization, they might become a permanent source of danger to America's political well-being and a menace to the very life of the nation.

"I have quoted from Professor Haskin because I feel deeply that he is right."

"One would think that Esther Winge came over in the 'Mayflower.'" There was a sarcastic edge in the tone of the speaker.

I turned, smiling, to the young man and said, "I told you that you would not agree with me. I am born a patriot, although I did not know it until, on board the Lusitania, I saw the shoreline of England disappear below the horizon and heard half a dozen national anthems sung around me. It was then my patriotism wept itself into consciousness. Since then I have known that I am Swedish. My patriotism has been blind, narrow. Tonight it has widened into an understanding for a nation with a vastly greater problem than my own. When I came here tonight I had no idea that I could feel as I am now feeling or say what I have just said."

"It's an altogether different point of view than the one we discussed a while ago," said Nathan. "We have several Communists among us, and we were discussing America as the ideal place for realizing the ideals of communism."

"I know so little about them," I replied.

Vera and Maria now entered with refreshments, and conversation became general. It was midnight before anyone made a move to leave, and then Nathan again took the floor and asked how many would like to attend the weekly concert in Orchestra Hall on Saturday nights. He said we could go in a group, and someone could buy the tickets for all. The suggestion was received with great enthusiasm. Everybody wanted to go. It was decided to change the fellowship meeting to Wednesday nights. A second suggestion that also met with approval was that all discussions should be carried on in the English language and that every one should write an essay on some popular subject and read it before the club. We were asked to write down a subject on a slip of paper. Someone brought a hat, gathering the slips, and then there was a "drawing." Since many of the subjects were similar, it took quite a while before each of us had one. It was almost two in the morning when Maria and I said good-night to our host and hostess. But long after we had turned off the light we talked quietly together.

Once Maria said, laughingly, "I never would have dreamed that I one day would love a Swede. In my childish fancy the Swede stood for everything that was dangerous and cruel. As little children we were told, when misbehaving, that the Swede would get us."

"How funny! That's just exactly what we were told about the Russian."

———

Again it is night. In a way the night seems to belong to me more than the day. Then I can think and dream, undisturbed. True, I can hear in the distance the muffled roar from the never resting metropolis, but this time of the night it is like the back roll of a storm. It does not excite. It only reminds me of the reality that will test the quality of my dream.

Life! I thank you for your gifts! Make me worthy of the gifts and the giver! Let my soul grow big and strong enough to embrace all you send with love's understanding!

October 5

BILL, the little hunch-backed elevator boy, has his ideas. Today, when we happened to be alone, going up, he said, "What are you doing here?"

"Here? I am going to my work."

"What is your work?"

"Hats."

"I don't believe it."

"If you don't believe me, ask someone else."

"I have, but I still don't believe it."

"What a skeptic! And why shouldn't I be capable of making hats?"

"I didn't say that you weren't capable, only that you are something else, nurse or something."

"Why should a nurse make hats?"

"That's what I'd like to know."

"I am not a nurse."

"What are you, then?"

"A factory worker."

"Why?"

"If you mean that factory work is not as respectable as any other kind of work, I will never speak to you again!"

"Ah, don't be silly!"

"Why do you think I am something else?"

"I have seen thousands of factory workers, day in and day out for ten years. I know them."

"In what way am I different?"

"I can't exactly say, but I'll bet my life you were not born to be a factory worker."

"No one was ever born to that, Bill. That's our conscription for tomorrow's dream."

There was a knowing grin on his face as he opened the door and said, "Just the same, I know I'm right."

And now, I suppose, I will always think of him as an unusually intelligent lad. He could appreciate *me!*

October 10

I PITY the man who has no pressing duty when the day begins and who has accomplished nothing when the day is done.

October 12

EVERY new morning the day lies before me like an unwritten page, and every evening I weep inwardly over the imperfections of the script.

October 13

IT WAS a morning as dismally gray as only Chicago can produce. A low fog hung like an impenetrable ceiling over the city, and the belching smoke, finding no vent, was pressed down until the atmosphere was so heavy that one could scarcely breathe. The throat burned, the eyes smarted, the nostrils were coated with soot. It was dark until noon, when the sun finally conquered the fog. As the first rays penetrated the ceiling, it was as if a draft had suddenly been opened. In a few moments the air was clear.

Maria came right after lunch, and we strolled along Lincoln Park Boulevard as close to the water as we could get. Fleecy clouds drifted over the deep blue sky, and light and shadows played tag over Lake Michigan's wide, shimmering surface.

Maria loves this walk. It reminds her a little of the old home by the Black Sea. In glowing words she paints the beauty of that scene, its colors, its clearness, its ever changing moods.

We had walked in silence, arm in arm, for some time when Maria suddenly said, "There is something I have been wanting to ask you. I have carried it a long time, but there is something about you that forbids my asking. I don't know why you always avoid speaking on the subject. What is your opinion about God?"

"God? Perhaps I have no ready opinion."

"There it is again! Sometimes I feel I have your full confidence, that your soul is before me as an open book. Then suddenly, you are draped in reserve, drawn within yourself like a snail in its shell. Why don't you want to speak about this subject? You have thought on practically every question that has been brought up. You must have thought about this also. You have been raised a Christian. But you are not a Christian now. Still, I don't know what you are."

"Perhaps I don't know myself."

"I don't believe that. That you don't want to speak on the subject I understand. But why you don't want to is beyond me. Anyone as free from prejudice as you are could not harbor any mystic superstition."

"How free I am from prejudice we'd better leave unsaid. I wonder if anyone dares to claim that he is free from prejudice? Doesn't the very expression 'mystic superstition' indicate a prejudice against a world inaccessible to my five senses?"

"You believe, then, in such a world?"

"Believe is not the word. Belief is something positive, a conviction resting on an unshakable foundation. With me everything is questions and doubts. While in college—and a couple of years after—I openly classified myself as a skeptic. As so many others before me, I thought I could untie the Gordian knot by cutting it off. I fought ruthlessly against superstition. I rejected blindly and wounded blindly. Every time I inflicted a wound on another, I stabbed myself. Soon my soul was immersed in suffering. Just as the adherents of Christian Science, in spite of their denial of the existence of pain and death, must open their doors and carry out their dead, and never hesitate to call on the dentist when a tooth aches, and can't hold back a cry of anguish when a bared nerve is touched, so I discovered that a fact is not nullified by my refusal to accept it. I began to doubt my own doubts. My arguments became

32

more impassioned and implacable, for I argued to convince myself."

"I don't understand. Did you want to believe what you didn't believe?"

"I am conscious only of one will, the will to truth. But as I tried to say, truth was not an indivisible whole that I could find in the camp of the skeptics. Confined within the boundaries of Christian dogma, I was compelled to violate my reason, but well outside its boundaries I found myself violating something within my being as essential to a balanced life as reason."

"That's easily explained. You were raised in dogma and superstition. You could not without struggle get free from something that had become your second nature."

"But, don't you see, that's the heart of the whole matter! If I had been raised in such an environment that a materialistic philosophy had become my second nature, how then could I objectively have appraised my own or the opposing philosophy?"

"Granted. But if something within me is divine, it certainly must be my intellect. It was your intellect that led you to renounce the Christian way although you had been brought up in its teachings. To me that is conclusive proof of its error."

"You are flattering my puny intellect. I know of personalities—past and present—so brilliant that in comparison with their intellect mine is as a speck of dust in relation to the universe. Nevertheless they are ardent believers in Christianity."

"On some point they have denied or ignored reason. That is the only explanation."

"It does not satisfy me. Has it never occurred to you that we who deny the reality which is the central point of their existence may have amputated the feelers that would have enabled us to become aware of the other world?"

"Evidently you still have them. I never dreamed that you were so much of a mystic. But I know no more about your idea of God than before. The only thing I know is that you doubt your own doubts. When did you begin to doubt?"

"My own doubts?"

"No, I mean when did your doubting start?"

"It was long, long ago. I was only a child. Mother had always been frail. She suffered from periodic headaches. Sometimes she sat up in bed all night with terrific pain. One night I woke up and saw her so. My thoughts went to Jesus. I had started school, where we had compulsory Bible teaching. That day I had heard the story about one who had been a cripple for thirty-eight years and was healed by Christ. I thought, if only He were here now, Mother would not have to suffer any more, for I would ask Him to make her well. Then I remembered that Mother had told me—often—that He was as near as if I could see Him outwardly and that His power was greater than ever because He was the Conqueror of death, and He was now at the right hand of God, in Heaven. I began to pray. I remember the whole incident as clearly as if it had happened yesterday. I remember every word in my prayer, 'Dear Lord, You healed the lame man, and Mother says that You are the same today. Won't You please heal Mother's headache?' I had been praying with hands folded and eyes closed. I remained so for a few moments to allow time for answer. Then I looked over to Mother's bed. She sat with both hands covering her face. Her whole body was convulsed with her sobs. Tears trickled between her fingers down on the quilt. Disappointment and anguish seemed to choke me. Again I prayed, 'Jesus, I know I can't pray right; I know I have not been good; please forgive me and heal Mother.' Again I looked. There was no change. Despair and anger held me. I clenched my fists now, 'Jesus, if You don't heal Mother now, I won't believe that You can. If You don't heal Mother now, I don't care for You. I am not praying for my own sake, for I am not good, but Mother is! Oh, Mother is so good! Do it for Mother's sake!' When the answer did not come, I crawled under the quilt and burst into tears. Since then—"

I happened to look up to Maria and saw her face wet with tears. I smiled and continued, "Often that memory has brought tears to my own eyes. There is something so heartrendingly hopeless in a child's first great sorrow and disappointment. The relative is unknown in the world of a child. Everything is absolute. When confidence is broken, the world collapses."

"You never believed after that?"

"Oh, yes! It is unnatural for a child to sorrow long. But it took a long time before everything was as before. Perhaps nothing was ever just the same. For a long time I felt that I was carrying a dreadful secret. I couldn't talk to Mother about it because I was sure it would bring her sadness. I had no brothers or sisters to talk to, and I did not dare to speak to any of my friends or schoolmates. The most difficult part was my relationship to God. Not to say my prayers at night was unthinkable. But for ever so long I felt that I had committed an unpardonable sin and that God would not hear me. I heard a great deal about Jesus, but I feared Him. And yet, it was impossible not to love Him. But my love for Him was more like the love for the hero in a book than for a living person.

"Not until the death of my mother—I was then twelve—did I rediscover Him as a living friend. Mother said that she was going to Him. She was fully conscious until the end. Father and I were alone by the deathbed. They loved each other deeply. I never heard a word of disagreement or misunderstanding between them. Their love for one another was so strong and full of reverence that it lifted the loved one to a holy place. In spite of that, it seemed to me, each of us was alone, shut off from others. It was as if each of us was surrounded by a circle of emptiness that no one could penetrate, as if we were stars, speeding on in boundless space, near each other, in the same direction, but hopelessly apart.

"I can't talk about Mother's last hour—never have, but this I want to tell you, so that you can understand how I came to believe. Mother put her hand on my head and said, 'God bless you, my own child! May Christ be your life, as He is mine!' Then she closed her eyes, but soon opened them again, only now she looked beyond Father and me to Another. Her eyes were as full of light and joy as if she looked upon One infinitely dear that she had long waited for. She reached out her arms, and her face became radiant, as if reflecting a great light."

There was a long silence, then Maria asked softly, "Your father, was he—"

"I don't know. He was very different. We were alone now. He was teaching and I had finished the secondary grades under him. I stayed at home and kept house for him. He had a dread of strangers and preferred to help with the chores around the house rather than having someone come in. He spent much time with me. We strolled together through the woods with our botanical tins; we listened to the call of the birds and learned to imitate them; we stood breathlessly still and watched the play of the grouse; we befriended the squirrels, and on clear nights we studied the stars. I say 'we.' Father had a way of studying with me that made me forget he was the teacher. We seemed to discover things together. When we read a book of travel, it always seemed we were on a journey. When we read a poem, it took on new meaning through the background father gave of the poet's life or the historic setting. History became the adventures of the human race throughout the ages. Geography was ever an explorer's expedition.

"Often father let me help him correct papers and make the last copy of his lectures so that we might gain time for our studies. But he never talked to me directly about God. That he believed in God I never doubted, but I sensed that his faith differed from Mother's. In what way, I didn't know. My religious life was very intimate at this time. As far as I could understand, I wanted Christ to be my life, as He had been Mother's. There was a deep-moving—although on my part childish—transaction between us. And as a human relationship deepens in tenderness after confession and forgiveness, so this otherworldly friendship was more closely tied after the removal of the long misunderstanding.

"The relativity of things began to grow on me at this time. Perhaps my heritage from Mother had been a strongly religious nature. It was easy for me to talk to Jesus. Never a day did I neglect to read my Bible, and I followed Mother's method of underscoring in red what particularly appealed to me. Often I was supremely happy. Unspeakable peace filled my soul. I longed to talk to Father about it, but I never could. Then I was confirmed in the state church. It was my own choice. Father told me I didn't have to do it if I didn't want to, but that if I wanted to enter a state teacher's college, it was compulsory. It was then I met the crisis that possibly laid the foundation for my skepticism. It had to do with infant baptism. I had not been baptized. The church said that I was a heathen and that Mother and Father were heretics. But Mother and Father belonged to those things in my life that were absolute. Therefore the church was wrong.

"In mother's Bible I found a verse underscored in red, 'He that believeth and is baptized shall be saved; but he that believeth not shall be damned.' I took that verse to my pastor. What he said made me doubt the honesty or intelligence of the church. How could I continue in the confirmation class after that? Defiance pushed me on. I wanted to become a teacher. The church could not stop me. If it was dishonest against the Word of God, how could it sit in judgment over my dishonesty? But it cost my peace. A couple of times I thought I heard the word 'Jesuit' behind my back. Self-accusations, hate, anger, defiance succeeded each other in my soul. Intimate conversations with Christ became infrequent. Once I spoke to Father about it. 'Could it be sinful,' I asked, 'to participate in a church ordinance for the sake of attaining a future goal?' He looked at me searchingly and long, then he looked out through the window a long time. Finally he said, very quietly, 'What does the god within you say?'—'The god within me?'—He smiled. 'Was that difficult to understand? One of our own philosophers uses it.'—'You mean conscience?' He nodded. I broke into tears. He drew me close until I had quieted down. Then he stroked my hair and said, 'My little daughter will choose the right.' But she didn't.

"Love for Father, longing to attain quickly a cherished goal, and disdain for the church decided my action. I was confirmed without answering, or by answering with reservation, the usual public questions. But something broke within me that hour. It is as if my soul has had a broken wing ever since. I can never forget that I betrayed truth in my first great crisis. Doubt after doubt found anchorage in my soul. Then suddenly the memory of Mother and her last hour would flash before me. How I hated myself! There

38

was reconciliation upon reconciliation, followed by new doubts and new reconciliations."

In silence Maria and I stood by the water's edge and watched the effortless wingbeats of the sea gulls. There was an urgency within me that made me continue.

"Strange, that just today I happened to open an old diary from those days. Every other page is filled with glowing declarations of unwavering faith, and every alternate one filled with questions. It was as if some insidious disease had overtaken me with its attacks becoming more frequent and its malignancy spreading as time passed. The doctrine of the Trinity had long puzzled me when *What the Bible Teaches About Christ* by Victor Rydberg came into my hands. It performed the most painful of all operations in my spiritual life: it separated Christ from God. Rydberg was my favorite writer. He was to me the indisputable authority. How Father and I had enjoyed his poems and *The Gunsmith!* - - - Life was more and more difficult. It called for so much strength. And everything was so relative. But God was still God.

"Then—it was the summer of my seventeenth birthday —came the great catastrophe. Father was away for a conference. Into my hands came a book by Robert Ingersoll and a letter from an idolized friend in Uppsala in which she stated that she could not answer my questions. She said she knew nothing, believed nothing. A suffering like that you can't talk about. I knew only one thing: I had to talk to Father. But a telegram came telling of his death.

"I wonder if you can understand that doubts and faith are intertwined in me? I have no anchorage. My only answer to all your questions is a simple 'I don't know.' But deep within me there is a hope that sometimes borders on certainty that TRUTH, unqualified, absolute, exists. Some people seem to be able to live without foundation, without

39

finding a meaning in their existence, a meaning that somehow transforms the struggle and the suffering into a sublime purpose. I can't. If you can tell me why I am like that, you have also found the answer to life's riddle. But if you can't, you have to admit that a world exists which is inaccessible to your reason or your five senses. The day I would know beyond doubt that such a reality did not exist, I would take my own life. But the day my soul found anchorage in that reality I would become invincible."

———

Why did I open to Maria a door that I always have guarded so carefully against intrusion? Why did I display before her skeptical eyes something I have always so anxiously protected? Did honesty demand it? No. Every one has a right to his own holy of holies. Why then did I do something that I knew would bring me unrest and regret? Did I seek her sympathy? The price for that sympathy would have been too high. I acted on impulse. To attempt an analysis of the impulse would only be guesswork, and it would not quiet my uneasiness. But if Maria's sympathy could be awakened in a way that would cause her to think—a little bit—with her heart instead of her head, then the price you paid, Esther Winge, would not be too high. Someone's soul must bleed if the Palovskys of this world are to be saved.

October 19

AGAIN it is night. I have read Ibsen's *The Wild Duck* in English. A splendid satire on mawkish idealism. One marvels over the accumulation of "nothingness" in Hjalmar Ekdal and one gets screaming, kicking mad over the inertia that has smothered all manliness in him and his household. Ralling, the realist, is the only wide-awake one—and him one hates.

40

October 20

OH BILL, BILL! How far the great have fallen. Here I was thinking that you were a deep philosopher and I a most exceptional person. And now it turns out that you are only a shrewd businessman and I a conceited woman. How can I forgive you? It would be interesting to know on how many you have tried that trick. Keep right on, Bill! I am sure you will succeed in selling your shares—or lots—or whatever it is. Not that I am as good a judge of men as you are, but good enough to prophesy that you will not end your days as elevator boy in a factory. You are made for America, and America is made for you. If you will be a railroad magnate, political boss, or king of industry, I can't say, but some day you will be seated behind a plate-glass door bearing your name in gold. Don't forget your conscription years then, years behind the gratings of an elevator, Billy-boy!

Or am I mistaken in this also? Is my conceit so apparent that an ordinary little elevator boy can detect it?

October 25

I CAN'T PLAY the simplest melody without mistakes, and still music is indispensable to me. It liberates my soul from the limitations of time and space.

Saturday evening has become the magic hour, the secret spring that gives buoyancy and fortitude for a week of gray days. Steep is the climb up the five flights to the top shelf of Orchestra Hall, but merry is the chatter before the lights are dimmed and the first notes ascend from the orchestra, far, far below. Then tired eyes close to the world of things and open to a world of fantasy and dreams.

When the music swells, imperious, wild, rapturous, submerging every single voice, then I know it is a magnificent harmony of all the world's suffering and exultation, laughter

41

and tears. But when a lonely, tremulous tone separates itself from all the rest and plaintively speaks of its seclusion, then I know it is my own soul singing. And when this tone quivers and dances like sunbeams over the waves, like the frolic of elves over lonely moors, then I know my soul is dreaming, forgetting its aloneness.

No, I don't "understand" music. When the critics praise or blame, I am silent. I don't know anything about the technique of musicians. But when, under the influence of music, crippled, tired thoughts take wings and the struggle takes on meaning and life becomes beautiful; when I forget where I am and vaguely sense what I am; when the melody finds its text in my own soul, then I want to say, "Thank you!" But my hands are as still as my lips.

Potpourri.

Climbing—climbing—alpine summits—climbing—! Immeasurable, singing silence. Thoughts set free—expanding. Suddenly mighty organ music vibrates within. A boundlessness like that without is felt. - - - Then the soul becomes a violin with a single string, keyed so high that its tone is fragile, elfin - - - but in minor—in minor - - - -

Psalm-melodies - - intonations throbbing with pain - - with suppressed tears - - - with baffled, unutterable longing. - - Jubilant hope of a visioned heaven - - - exultation and tears - - longing and hope - - - rhythm—rising and falling - - a psalm-melody.

Only sleigh bells break the singing silence in an endless, snowladen forest. Thoughts grow still and find repose as whirling snowflakes, settling down under towering firs, become a part of a shimmering whiteness, suggestive of infinite stillness and peace. - - - - A slight sound, a whispering breeze, a glade, a little lake, carpeted with a billion sparkling diamonds. - - - Mountain peak after mountain

42

peak, rising in dazzling splendor, suffused with sunlight.
- - - Sun setting, leaving behind a slowly vanishing, rosy
glow. Then all is white, the blue whiteness of the mountains only faintly distinguishable from the white of the
sky. Ethereal, as if made of condensed light, they remind
you in their unsullied purity of smiling baby lips or a
mother's kiss. They awaken the soul's yearning for purity,
for wider horizons, for more clarity; they awaken the
spirit's longing to reach the alpine summits of lofty thinking.

> Am I not myself the child
> Of sun and snow
> That in singing unrest is seeking its sea?

Violin! Stop your questionings, your lamentation! They
are living, quivering heart strings that you are strumming.
It hurts! Your questions are unanswerable. I am weary of
them. - - - Where did you get that strain, violincello? You
speak with authority, as if you knew the answer to life's
secrets.

"Be still, and know that I am God." God? Thus He must
speak if He is. Speak, cello! What do you know about God?
Is He the One that with a word flung the worlds into endless space and sent time awandering toward eternity? Is
He the all-knowing One who willed that millions upon
millions should be born to endless suffering and an eternity
of doom? Does He speak like that? Then I have not understood Him. Only One whose love is as great as His
power can speak in that fashion! "Be still, and know that
I am God." There it is again! One voice without compare,
transcendent in glory and power, making all other voices
melt into an accompaniment of sublime harmony. - - - -
- - - - Even if the wellsprings of life gush forth from
depths you never can fathom, and their streams flow out
and on, far, far beyond your vision, what of it? - - I AM.

43

And are you not yourself a drop of its ceaseless flow? Why not rest in ME? I am the SOURCE of ALL, its ultimate meaning and goal. I alone rest in MYSELF. There is no beginning, no cause beyond ME. - - -

But why - - why - - why, then?

All questions, all doubts, all voices drown in overwhelming, surging, jubilant symphony.

October 28

WHAT a power prayer has ever been in my life! Up until the day when—driven by torturous doubt—I concluded that a personal God did not exist, I can't remember an evening when I did not kneel by my cot saying my prayers. And after that day, how absolutely essential it became to find a substitute for prayer! (Sometimes I wonder if the thing substituted was not in reality prayer.) Often when night approaches I have a melancholy feeling of being alone in a cavernous house in a deep forest. So deep-rooted can a habit become. Or is it more than a habit? Is there a deep within, calling to another deep? Who can answer?

Free? No! Perhaps I never can be. How could I go back months before I was born and free myself from the spiritual heritage of mother? I was born in prayer. Even my disavowal of Christianity was a prayer, come to think of it. "I am going to live as if God existed—as if my every action were to be judged by Him. It will be up to me to decide on which side of the scales my action falls. For that decision I need honesty and strength. Give it to me, Life!"

Night after night since then, I have summed up—and audibly spoken—my inmost desire. What is that if not prayer?

November 4

STRIKE! I am a striker!

The motor had been started, as usual, at twelve thirty,

44

but its humming was the only sound that could be heard. The women, more than one hundred of them, sat motionless in their places. The foreman came rushing from the office, his face scarlet, and demanded, "What's the matter? Why aren't you working?" No answer. "Don't be silly, girls! This is pure foolishness. You are just wasting precious time both for yourselves and the firm." No one moved or answered. Then his glance touched me. He came over and with a voice hoarse with emotion he whispered, "You will pay for this, Esther Winge."

Only a few heard the words. Maria Palovsky was one of them. She sprang to her feet. "You are wrong, Mr. Miller, Esther Winge has nothing to do with this. It's a sympathy strike."

"Sympathy strike! Sympathy with what, for whom?"

Maria replied, "We will not return to work until you have satisfactorily answered Esther's request for the Slavonian women."

"What concern is that of yours? What has Esther Winge got to do with it?" With an oath he turned and ordered the motor to be stopped.

"Sympathy strike." The words had wings and went from mouth to mouth. There had been a general feeling that an injustice was being perpetrated and that somehow it must be prevented. Without exception, the workers were willing to give up an hour or two, if needed. But when Miller asked the reason, no one had a ready answer. Half of the strikers didn't even know what it was about. Maria gave the password. It was probably new to most of them. Perhaps many felt rather than sensed its meaning, but its very newness had a magical effect. It called forth heroism. Those who had been willing to give up the earnings of an hour or two were now willing to give up a few days if necessary.

To me the whole spectacle had an element of greatness.

45

It brought exultation. I don't clearly know why, but it reminded me of the first time I looked at the world from the summit of a very high mountain. I saw only sweeping lines. Today I saw in a moment's clear vision the proletariat of all the world marching on in complete accord, in humble surrender of petty, personal interests, imbued with a sense of solidarity and brotherhood that foreshadows the dawn of a new day. It was like an emancipation.

It all happened so quickly. Yesterday afternoon one of the Slavonian women came over to me and in her broken English asked how much I could make on the type of work I was doing, which was like theirs. I told her that at the present I was making samples for which I was paid by the hour with 50 percent added. She looked disappointed and said that for the past few days they had been given the same kind of work, but as piecework and at such low prices that they could only make half as much as they usually do in the busy season.

I knew that they were exceptionally competent workers who had learned the trade in their native land and that they were much in demand in America. I realized they were correct in their assumption that only their inability to express themselves in English was the reason for the treatment they had received. They had hoped I would speak for them. Thinking it over for a while, I gave them my word.

At first the foreman attempted to make a joke of it. But when he saw that I was serious, he became ingratiating and persuasive. Why should I worry about the rest? Didn't I have nice work and wasn't I satisfied with my wages?—Yes, but I can't stand that others should not be treated the same way.—However, hadn't I come for the purpose of making money? He, the foreman, would certainly see to it that I made as much as anyone. Why should I interfere with other people's business?

I told him that I was determined to keep my promise. Would he, therefore, seek an agreement with the manager? When he saw that nothing else would do, he promised that he would. This answer somewhat quieted the Slavonian women. They decided to keep on working until the answer came. It didn't come all afternoon, and my repeated question received only evasive answers.

This morning I again asked what had been decided. "Nothing," he said. "It is impossible for us to raise the price on these particular hats. We get so little for them that if we pay more we will lose."

"I am not here to criticize your business methods, but I object to what they lead to. The women I have been asked to represent refuse to do this work until they get better pay."

"There is one thing we can do. We can reduce prices on other types of work in order to raise them on this."

At this moment the manufacturer, who was seldom seen, entered the room. Without a moment's hesitation I walked up to him and said, "Mr. Miller refuses to consider our request for a more reasonable price on Milan hemp. Is that your desire?"

"I don't know anything about it. Didn't know anyone was dissatisfied. Will speak to Miller."

After I had given my report, they decided not to work until the answer had come. After a while Miller came to me and said that all would be arranged to the satisfaction of all if they only would go to work again. The answer would come within an hour. I told him of the decision of the Slavonian women not to work until they had heard. Three hours passed. No answer. When I returned from a brief walk after lunch, the strike was general.

After the motor had been stopped, Miller got up on a chair and beckoned to all to come closer. He tried hard to speak calmly, but it was easy to see that anger boiled within him. They must have misunderstood the whole matter. No injustice had been intended. Milan hemp would be paid as well as any other work, but they must give him time to work out the problem.

Someone called out, "You have had time, and you have broken your promise several times. How do we know that you won't do it again?"

"And how," someone else asked, "will you work it out? Perhaps by cutting prices on other work?"

His face turned a deep red. Oh, so Esther had had time to bear tales! Surely they realized that it was only a joke! The motor will be started again, and the sensible ones can go back to work. The others had better go home until they come to their senses.

Again the motor hummed. Suddenly the sharp whirring of a power machine cut through. It was like an electric shock. Every face turned toward the sound.

"Mrs. Berg!"—"Traitor!"—"Shame!"—"Coward!"—"Strikebreaker!" The words came from all directions. And not words only. Soon the lone woman was pelted with empty spools, straw, balls of paper, and scraps of refuse. The foreman stood powerless. The only thing he could do was to shut off the motor and lead Mrs. Berg into the office.

Stunned, I watched the scene. Never have I felt less like smiling than when peal after peal of laughter accompanied successful "hits." The sweeping grandeur of the mountains was lost. There was suffocating qualm. Then anger rose within me. Couldn't they understand that a group of calm, sensible workers, demanding justice, would inspire respect, but that a bunch of jabbering, dirt-throwing kids would only arouse ridicule? I wanted to jump up on a chair and command quiet, but I knew that I would not be heard even by those closest to me. I am strong only in dreams and visions.

When the foreman returned, it was clear that the fight

was on. There was no returning. A new element had entered—desire for revenge. It was strong enough to push everything else in the background. Forgotten was the reason for starting the strike. All the unrest and dissatisfaction, all the suppressed longing for freedom and change, all the vague impulses that lead to restlessness now sought for expression in vengeance. "I'll never go back, as long as she is here!"—"You won't find me working alongside a traitor!"—"If you want her, count me out!"

Quite a group still hung around Miller, but most of the women—like myself—had entered the restroom, which was separated from the workroom by a six-foot partition. Alongside one wall there were several grimy washstands and along another, hooks for wraps. "What are we going to do now?" Maria asked one of the older, more experienced women.

She replied in a whisper, "I have phoned a union leader. There is a representative waiting for us downstairs."

Soon we were all gathered in the lower hall around a stoutish, middle-aged woman. Wasn't she a bit too elegant in her new fur coat? And wasn't there a trace of condescension in her patronage? Possibly I am wrong. My judgment is too often swayed by strong sympathy or unreasonable dislike. Most of the workers knew about the meeting, and no one could escape it. For whether they came down in the elevator or by the stairs, they were drawn into the crowd.

"Who is she?"—"What does she want?"—"Why is she here?"—"What does she get out of helping us?"

Suddenly the whispering ceased as Mrs. Morris, who was responsible for the meeting, clapped her hands for attention and said, "We have begun a strike today, and we want to win it. I took for granted that not one of us could manage the affair, so I took the liberty to call union headquarters and ask Mrs. Burns to come. She has led more strikes than the rest of us ever heard about, and she has won justice for thousands of workers. I know she can help us, if we follow her advice."

"Girls," Mrs. Burns said, "allow me to congratulate you! You have done a great thing today. It proves that you are independent and refuse to be stepped on. It is workers like you that will bring about better conditions. Now, the first thing you must do is to organize. Before you - - "

She was interrupted by a storm of words. "Organize!"— "Union!"—"No, no, no!"—"We have had enough of that!"— "We don't need your help."—"We know why you are here— to get our money!"—"You'll never catch me in a union again!" —"We can take care of ourselves!"

Once more it was quiet, and they all looked toward me. I don't know just how it happened, but an impulse stronger than my inborn reserve and timidity pushed me up to the top step to call for silence. I asked, "What do you want to gain with your strike?"

"Mrs. Berg must out!" It came from several.

"Is that all?"

"No, better prices." Again, several answered.

"Then let us talk it over like sensible women and not act like children. I turned to a well-dressed, younger woman with a beautiful, intelligent face and said, "Miss Young, you just said that you don't want to have anything to do with unions. How do you figure we can win the strike?"

"We send a delegation tomorrow to the firm to represent us and make our demands."

"Who sends a delegation?"

"We."

"Who are we? A bunch of individuals. If we are going to send a delegation, then the delegation must have something to represent. And how can we elect a delegation without some mutual understanding and unity? And what is mutual understanding and unity if not organization? Why are you afraid of a union? If it is our own, we make our own laws. It will be what we make it. Either this strike will be a fiasco, and the firm as well as all sensible people will make fun of us, or we follow Mrs. Burns' advice. It is the only way."

There was mumbling and whispers all around. Then one voice rose above the rest. "Esther is right. It's the only thing to do." Soon voices were heard from every direction. "Yes, of course it's right. anyone can see that. I am for it."—"I am too."—Rising tumult. Here and there a rebellious voice, silenced by other voices, arguing, pleading. Everybody seemed to talk at the same time. After consulting with Mrs. Burns and myself, Mrs. Morris once more called for attention and asked all who were willing to organize to raise their hands. It was difficult to determine how many failed to do it, so overwhelming was the majority. When those opposed were asked for the same sign, not a hand was raised. Were they ready now to listen to Mrs. Burns? A few yeas were heard.

Conscious that she still did not have their confidence, possibly also embarrassed over the extra audience, on the outside fringes of the crowd, Mrs. Burns quickly made her point. A hall down in the Loop was waiting for us, only a short distance away. We could walk there in a body.

Led by Mrs. Burns, we started off. Quite an interesting crowd it was. More than one pedestrian turned around to look at us. First came the older women, mostly mothers, supporting their own families. They were well but simply dressed and they walked with a certain dignity. Then followed the young American girls, dressed in the latest whim of fashion, with penciled eyebrows, sparkling "diamonds," and jaunty airs. For them it was a holiday and adventure. Last came a group of women, dressed in long, dark skirts, old-fashioned, threadbare coats, or fringed shawls, their

51

heads covered with dark kerchiefs. They were easily recognized as the Slavonian women, the indirect cause of the strike. Evidently they were greatly disturbed, gesticulating and talking excitedly in their own language, entirely unconcerned over their surroundings or attention of the onlookers.

Over one cross street after another we were carried along; over the oily, stinking, lazy river, in between the soot-blackened walls of the skyscrapers toward a small, dark hall on Washington Street, toward the realization of—what? A few "cog-dreams"? I cherished no illusions, but I was reminded of a thought that a few days ago caused me to lift up my head and take a new hold. "He that can remember, in the dark valley and the steep ascent the sweeping lines and uncluttered vision of the Summit, has learned fortitude."

I was elected to three tasks: temporary financial secretary (which means that I must write down all these queer names and difficult addresses); a member of the intermediary committee (which means that I must overcome my paralyzing timidity and appear before the public); and finally, to give a complete report of the strike, its causes and development, before tomorrow's meeting (which means that I will have to spend the rest of the night wrestling with English words).

November 12

THE STRIKE lasted a week. When it ended and everybody had returned to work, no one seemed inclined to talk about it or even with a facial expression show before the foreman the satisfaction that was felt over the results. A week's wages had been lost. There had been opportunity to have a little fun and to enjoy the fleeting pleasure of idleness, but the women had spent hours upon hours every day sitting in the dark, musty, ill-ventilated hall, just waiting.

52

So they were happy to return to work and, if possible, make up some lost time and wages. When the final report had been given, there had been a sudden burst of jubilation, applause, and cheers, but everyone had suffered in a measure and it was instinctively felt that it would be in bad taste to express satisfaction before one who had suffered infinitely more. It was whispered that Miller would have lost his job had it not been for the sake of his father, who for many years had been manager of the factory.

The results of the strike were surprising even to us who were members of the intermediary committee. We had hoped for better prices on some of the work. But in the proposal for settlement we had worked out, we demanded a 25 percent increase on all work, as well as a reasonable price on Milan hemp, as well as a closed shop, which meant that only union members would be given work. This, however, did not satisfy the craving for revenge that still possessed many. Mrs. Berg could not be forgotten. Were they expected to go back and work side by side with her who had been sitting by her machine, earning double wages? And was she now to be benefited by their victory? No, she had to go! This attitude hampered our negotiations. As a committee we could not speak with conviction. We lacked moral anchorage. The firm had the advantage over us. They advocated magnanimity. In vain I used what little persuasion I could muster. They would not listen to any talk about conciliation.

"What you say is good and beautiful, but it does not work in a struggle like this. We must use other methods. We must set an example."

Finally they agreed to compromise. Mrs. Berg would be permitted to join our union, but this could not take place except at a regular meeting, which would be in three weeks. With this change the firm accepted our proposal, and there was a settlement.

These were strenuous days. No one knows the price I paid in sleepless nights, in exhaustive mental concentration and desperate wrestling with words the meaning of which was felt rather than understood, as I prepared my brief statements and remarks. At times when I stood before them, I wondered why the women did not smile over my language. But they never did. Sometimes I see myself (as they must have seen me) and hear (as they must have heard) the stiff correctness of my sentences and the broken, foreign accent of my words. It made me self-conscious.

As if Maria had guessed it, she said to me one day, "Esther, I could have walked up, while you were speaking, and embraced you and kissed you! You speak with your whole face. It becomes a window with your soul looking out. Nathan is right. There is in your soul something of the fire Moses saw in the burning bush."

"I was afraid they would laugh at me."

"Laugh! Are you blind? Can't you see how still it gets when you begin to speak? Your earnestness is so great that you can make the most superficial feel it!"

What is more wonderful than a true friend? However, I must not forget that the appraisal of a friend is a reflection of his own goodness and not a reliable estimate of reality. Nevertheless, his appraisal possesses a reality with lifting power.

Like a weaver's shuttle the intermediary committee went back and forth between employer and employees until agreement was reached. In the hall they played and danced between the sessions. There was a little old organ in a corner, and always someone was at hand who knew a little dance music. The tango was the current fad. It always had a depressing effect on me to come in from the serious, often heated discussions and negotiations with the firm and find the girls swaying and gyrating amid clouds of dust in the ill-ventilated hall. Usually the music stopped as soon as some member of the committee appeared. We were always greeted with applause. But no applause could ward off the gloom I always felt at that sight. In my own heart I defended them. They didn't know any better. But I wept inwardly over my inability to arouse them and over the shortsightedness of their leaders. Why didn't they use these golden hours to inform, educate, and guide? Why didn't they call on some of the noble leaders of a certain organization to speak to the girls? The last question I asked Mrs. Morris, who had been elected president of our union. She gave me a strange look and said, "What do you know about them?" I said I knew some of them personally and regarded them highly. From that moment her attitude toward me changed. She became suspicious and disagreeable. I felt I had made an enemy without knowing why.

November 20

IT IS NOW CLEAR why the management was so conciliatory. Hardly had we returned to work before the strike broke out in other and larger factories. One strike was followed by another until practically all the workers in the trade had been organized. It would have been impossible for the factories to get skilled workers. They had to bow to necessity.

In our factory, however, things are not running smoothly. We haven't settled back into old grooves. A permanent intermediary committee has been elected to deal with lesser grievances and disputes. I was elected to this committee also. Few are the days when we are not called on. On the surface it looks like old times, but one is conscious of an inner tension. Mrs. Berg has not been around, but it is whispered that she has been denied work, wherever she has applied, and that she has repeatedly asked to be admitted to the union in order to get work. A bit of Americana fits the case well: "Nothing doing."

November 21

TODAY, right after lunch hour, I heard my name called. When I looked up, Miller was leaning over the table, asking me to come into the office. I followed him. There was a marked lull in the velocity of sound as we passed the long tables, and I met many questioning glances. But no one spoke. Entering the office I immediately noticed Mrs. Berg by the window. The personnel seemed busily occupied with typewriters and books, but furtive glances were turned my way as I entered and also during the conversation. Mrs. Berg looked so anxious and frightened that my heart went out to her. When I asked about her sick boy, her face momentarily lit up with a grateful smile.

After a moment's pause Miller said ingratiatingly, "Esther has more discernment than all the rest put together and that's why I thought we could talk things over between us. Here now is Mrs. Berg. She is willing to join the union at the next meeting. She is even willing to pay the dues in advance, if you will only let her work."

"Excuse me, Mr. Miller, if we are to change the contract already agreed upon, the committee as a whole must be called and a special meeting announced. I have no power to act alone."

"If you wanted to, you could do more than anyone else. Let us be reasonable now! Is it right and just to deprive an individual of the right to earn an honest living? It's paltry and revengeful."

"Certain conditions were agreed upon. You and I as

subordinate individuals have no other choice than to submit to facts."

"Esther, forget a moment that you are representative of a union. We won't quarrel with the heartless mass opinion of the organization. And we don't deny that it has its place, even can be necessary. But we are interested in what Esther Winge thinks on the subject."

"I was not elected to represent my personal opinions."

"I haven't called you as a union representative but as a thinking woman."

It had grown very quiet in the office. Our conversation had been carried on in low tones, but evidently not a word had been lost even to the errand-boy by the door. I felt strangely calm. My answer came without hesitation.

"If my personal opinions and convictions differ from those of the organization I represent, then I am hypocritical and have no right to be their representative."

"Does the organization forbid you to have personal opinions?" The tone was sarcastic.

I smiled and turned to Mrs. Berg to ask if she had received the report of the strike. She said she had and was very sorry over the whole thing. She never thought it was serious enough to develop into a strike, and she felt she could not afford to lose any time. Her mother wanted to come over to America and her little boy was sick, needing medical care. It took every penny she could scrape together. Besides, the foreman had told her the thing would be settled in a couple of hours and to the satisfaction of all. She hadn't known anything until spools and straw were flying around her.

"You must have forgotten, Mrs. Berg, that I spoke to you, asking your advice because you had so much experience, and you promised the same day the strike began to help us."

"Yes, I am not one to betray my fellow workers. I was an officer of a union for several years."

"That makes your behavior still more puzzling."

"But I was satisfied with the pay I received. I was working in three different factories this season, and in no place were prices so good. I told Mr. Miller that. Why shouldn't I say what was true?"

How could I help a feeling of contempt? "Are you willing, now that we have raised the prices 25 percent, to work after the old scale?" She was silent.

"Don't you realize, Mrs. Berg, that your unusual skill gives you an advantage? The management is anxious to keep you, and so they give you the best work available. When they pay out your fifty to sixty dollars a week—about three times the average pay, they have saved the cost of two machines. Is it any wonder they are anxious to keep you? And why shouldn't they give you the best? Did it never occur to you that prices that enable you to make a comfortable living are only sufficient for a mere existence for the average worker and mean starvation for the less skillful? To whom much has been given, of him the more will be demanded. We don't live for ourselves alone. We live in a society where one is dependent on another."

"Keep your sermons, Esther, they don't impress us. If anyone has done her duty, it's Mrs. Berg. She was loyal to her employer when the rest of you failed. She even told me that she felt her conscience would not let her act differently. I wonder how many of you paid any attention to your consciences?"

Suddenly I felt very tired. I looked from one to the other of these two, both of whom had lied to me. Were they false? Was it only hypocrisy for them to speak of conscience? Or did they honestly believe that I was hypocritical? Is TRUTH then something so general and indefinite

58

that it can be molded to fit any circumstances? Conscience? Yes, that is personal and hidden from view. Clearly, they had as much right as I have to assert their truthfulness. But did they? Is there no norm then for THE GOOD? Something valid for all and for all time? Motives are hidden. Who can appraise them? But the act? All could see that. In which balance did it fall, self-interest or the sacrifice of self in the interest of others—all others? New thoughts came surging.

"No authority ought to be greater than that of the conscience, but if my conscience would bid me to act contrary to the happiness of others and contrary to the higher law of the social conscience, then I would mistrust it and refuse to obey it."

While I was speaking the door opened and Mr. Gray, the big boss, entered. He looked questioningly from one to the other and asked wearily, "What's up now?"

Since Miller seemed at a loss for words I said lightly, "Mr. Miller asks us to temper justice with mercy for Mrs. Berg."

"Attend to your own business, Miller, and don't meddle with things that don't concern you."

"And you," he said, turning to Mrs. Berg, "for heaven's sake spare us more trouble. Come back when the powers that be permit you!"

"Are you satisfied now?" The words were directed to me in a tone half-jesting, half-annoyed, while he held the door open for me and smilingly bowed me out.

November 28

IT SOON became apparent to everyone that entered the factory Monday morning that something unusual had happened. Small cliques of women could be seen here and there, whispering and glancing furtively toward the empty chair by the foreman's desk. His father had died during the night from a heart attack. Sympathy and compassion pushed all other feelings into the background. Most of us realized that to Miller this meant more than the loss of his father. It would be difficult for him to keep his job after the one who had always covered up for him was gone. His father had been business manager of the plant for a long time. Although Miller was far from popular as foreman, pity was felt for him. At the same time there was embarrassment. The workers wanted to express their sympathy, but found it difficult to free themselves from the memory of the past weeks' experiences.

Around eleven o'clock he arrived. In his bearing there was the dignity a great sorrow usually lends to even the most shallow and selfish. Miller was not a great soul, so his dignity was mixed with an element of self-indulgence, as if he enjoyed a role that silenced criticism and called forth only sympathy and helpfulness. He had a story to tell that was evidently intended to arouse regret and pity. He claimed that the strike was the direct cause of his father's death. He had worried so much that his health broke under the strain. So now we stood accused of murder!

It was no secret, however, that the elder Miller was a heavy drinker and that he suffered from a serious heart ailment. His death had not come as a surprise to those who knew him. And we, who during the strike had been given a behind-the-curtain look into his business methods, could attest that he did not suffer from a finely drawn conscience. That anyone under the influence of a great sorrow could stoop to such smallness was beyond most of us. But we let it pass. Almost everyone contributed to the very beautiful wreath we sent. I was one of those sent out to represent the factory at the funeral.

A simple ceremony was held in the home of the deceased where there was a large gathering of relatives, friends, and others. The atmosphere was heavy with the scent of dying flowers. Every face wore its own mask of solemnity and real or simulated sympathy. But no mask could hide the color tone of the soul. It shone through. Everywhere one heard the usual, whispered comments: "Never have I seen such beautiful flowers."—"How peaceful he looks!"—"My, what beautiful flowers!"—"What an elegant casket! I wonder how much it cost?" The clergyman was a middle-aged man with an intelligent face. He had not known the departed, which accounted—to a certain extent—for the abstractness of his address. If you would learn to know a minister without asking personal questions, listen to his funeral orations. In the presence of the solemnity and finality of death, speculation is silenced. If the speaker knows a sure foundation, it becomes apparent. If not, his words are only poetic flowers woven into wreaths to hide inescapable facts.

He spoke of death as the entrance door to life, using the old text, "Except a corn of wheat fall into the ground and die, it abideth alone: but if it die, it bringeth forth much fruit." It was a beautiful speech. One couldn't help enjoying and admiring the well-chosen phrases and delicate imagery, unless, of course, he felt that he had been hopelessly separated from a being so close to him that he didn't know how life could go on without him. Many of us needn't have felt that way, and yet I did. My sorrow after father had never healed. Because of that my sympathy for the bereaved was so keen that I felt anger over the emptiness in the spoken word.

What relationship could there be between the facts that day follows night; spring, winter; flowers, frost; joy, sorrow; fruitfulness, pruning; and that a body once housing a soul whose whole aim and endeavor was material gain now was to be committed to earth and dissolved into atoms? It can't be denied that religion alone has comfort to offer. Not Buddhism with its endless transmigration of soul and eventual unconscious existence—Nirvana, and not Mohammedanism with a heaven that recognizes only sensual laws. Hope and comfort must come from Him who said, "I am the resurrection, and the life: he that believeth in me, though he were dead, yet shall he live." But this comfort is so conditional that one would never dare to mention it unsure that the condition had been met, and then this comfort were not needed. "He that hath the son hath life, and he that hath not the son shall not see life." Did they believe that, the Christians? Did he really believe that, this cultured, pleasant, sympathetic clergyman? Of course not! Had he believed it, he certainly would not have failed to use this made-to-order opportunity to plead in dead earnestness with his hearers to consider this most important step. I doubt that very many Christians do believe it. If they did, how could they so complacently watch neighbors, friends, and members of their own families speed headlong to eternal destruction? What puzzles me is that they so positively assert their faith in parts of the "Holy Word," while they completely ignore other parts. What principle do they follow in their division of the Bible? They never say.

The last flowery phrase of his speech died away without giving more light or comfort than the tolling of the bells or the fragrance of the flowers that were also a part of the funeral. The casket was carried out, and the mourners followed, huddled together like a flock of helpless children.

December 15

ABOVE ALL ELSE I must learn that it is the principle, not the person, I must serve. When a duty brings me in close

62

contact with uncongenial people, when my work is under-rated, my motives misinterpreted, and my ability questioned, I am ready to throw everything overboard. That is one of my many great weaknesses.

December 20

A BEAUTIFUL, tall vase, filled with velvety, red roses, is standing on my poor little table. For two days I have been oblivious to pain and weakness in the gladness and harmony of that beauty. It caresses me. My thoughts grow tranquil and bright. I believe I have blessed the fever and weariness that tied me to the bed. Lillie, the prettiest and proudest of the young American girls in the factory, brought the gift the second day of my illness. She said, "It's from all of us but especially from the Slavonian women. They sent a special greeting that they love you and that you won the strike for them." It was not I who won the strike, but who would not revel in friendship's overrating?

December 24

CHRISTMAS EVE! Day of memories! How could I spend you with strangers? It is better to be alone with you and joys of long ago.

How beautiful you were, my childhood yuletide! Father, mother, and I and our great love. Your beauty was such that its memory calls forth more thankfulness than sadness, and my thankfulness grows until I can hardly stand it. It seems to me there *must* be Someone at whose feet I can lay it down. It is when I think of all the good and glad things of life that I miss God most. When my gratitude grows and grows until it seems like a rising, flooding tide, it seems unreasonable that there is no one to receive it, as if my lovely, red roses had to bloom without ever having been seen, their exquisite fragrance never known. That is where the hopeless emptiness of atheism comes in. But, says Maria, that is only inherent prejudice, morbid fantasy. Is she right? I wish I knew. One of us is mistaken.

Christmas Day

SPENT the afternoon with Maria. In the gathering twilight we could not distinguish each other's faces. A great tranquillity enveloped me. The patter of the rain against the window was loud and incessant. The sound of water splashing down the gutter became a pleasing accompaniment to her low voice. I only half listened—dreamed and remembered. It does one good to feel like an honored guest—not always a stranger.

December 26

LEARN TO WILL—what you MUST! The way to freedom lies in that direction.

December 27

PRAISE and recognition is the elixir of life to me. I am good for nothing without it. Let someone express an honest —or even an unpremeditated—opinion to the contrary, and they lower my ambition, rob my vitality. I have absolutely no more faith in myself than I receive from others.

December 29

READ one of Tolstoy's stories tonight. Each of them is a fragment of reality. They seldom are "finished." Life itself is like that. We enter it, playing our puny parts in its drama, and leave it, pulsing, acting, flowing. Whereto? Wherefrom? Why?

December 30

To THE POOR, money is the polestar in which all human passions find their center. Not to be poor, nor rich; not to owe anyone anything, and not to covet anything—that is to have reached the borderland where life is beautiful and sorrow sweet.

Some people never fit in. Can they help it? A young oak, growing crooked against the unyielding cliff, may be transplanted—and survive, but it will never be straight. Is it thus souls are shaped in their cradles? And the "straight" cannot understand the "bent."

New Year

AGAIN I find myself within the realm of melancholy's dark enchantment. It's like being shut out—or in. I am absolutely alone. Friendly smiles and words are powerless to reach me. I talk and act like an automaton.

What is it we long for? I stood by a window, looking out over Lake Michigan's wide, mist-shrouded expanse and said to myself, "Over there, in the dim distance, are the people I long for." It may be true, but not the whole truth. One longs forever. And the thing one for the moment misses seems to be the object for one's longing, but the object obtained does not bring completeness. The longing persists. Were I this moment encircled by the arms of those I long for, an inner restlessness would compel my eyes to search for new horizons.

January 5

THREE flattened pieces of butterscotch inside the covers of a book from Sweden made me happier than I have been for a long time. But oh, the nostalgia!

January 10 on the streetcar

To BE AROUSED suddenly by the alarm clock every morning and never allowed to sleep until one wakes up does not make one's spirit soar exactly. Better get the habit of beating the alarm!

It is a brisk, glorious, winter morning. The sun is just

rising, a ball of fire beyond purple clouds. The streetcars are always crowded, morning and night. Everybody is reading. Mostly newspapers. They sit and read. They stand and read, if there is no place to sit. I seldom sit. And I seldom read. I have to look at all the types riding with me—and think. Some are really amusing. As for instance, the conductor this morning with his red, round face and his coat in tatters. - - - Amusing? Possibly not, if I could look behind the mask. No one's life is a comedy. It is easy to look impersonally at a stranger and forget that he is an individual like myself, struggling, suffering, failing, longing —like me. - - - It could be that did I know the story of the tattered coat I would weep—and not laugh.

Have been scanning the pages of a book I received for Christmas. What senseless twaddle! Spiritual mishmash, superstition, lunatic ramblings! Seldom have I felt such aversion for a book. I long for strength—uncompromising, clean! - - - A love, demanding all, and giving all. I am tired of sulkiness and grumbling and lukewarmness, of half truths and hide-and-seek games! I want reality, the naked truth, unbending honesty, soul-shaking sincerity. But vapid, humdrum hours pursue their snail-like pace. In a few minutes I will drop into the treadmill as a tiny cog among all the other little cogs. The big machinery that furnishes the motive power for the ever grinding mill will roar and surge. The individual machines will cut through with their shrill treble. And I will sew—sew—sew—for dear life, while world-uplifting dreams drown in tears of desperation over the apathy of mankind.

And who am I? A Lilliputian who can't even control herself? If only I could make a clean break with conventionalities and be myself! But not me! How could I be myself? I, who live in others, and let others live in me; I, whose moods fluctuate with the unpredictable winds of flattery or censure; I, who become clever, because others consider me so; who act thus and so, because it is expected of me. - - - I always know—afterwards—what I *should* have said, how I *should* have acted!

May 26

OUT OF HIDING, old book! Let me speak up, or something will break! Let me put my thoughts into order, or I will lose myself!

It is religion again. When was it not? It is the old conflict between "the god within and the god without"—to speak with Hans Larson. A Protestant church with restfulness and harmony in music and atmosphere, and its pastor, Dr. E., has been the central point around which my life has moved now for four months. There must be a decision. Religion can not be the objective of life but rather a means whereby life is made richer, more beautiful, yes, even possible to endure. Therefore I can't forever let my thoughts circle around this little haven, as if life's sum and substance could be found in forgetfulness of a world that is far from harmonious. Were I a Christian I would go to church to receive strength for my workaday task. Now that I am not a Christian my churchgoing may have motives unacceptable to the god within.

—Let's see, Esther Winge, why do you go?

—Because all my being is filled with uncontrollable longing, I am alone and tired—and my life has no meaning—and I lack the strength needed to accomplish, succeed. And in that little church there is light, not garish or blinding, but mellow and restful. The carpets and pews are soft, the melodies are sweet, and people are there who believe. There is peace in their eyes and a song on their lips. Everything I lack is there, and I am so weary a wanderer. I go there to rest.

—Is rest the highest good of life?

—I don't think so, but I don't know what it is.

—You don't know, and yet you allow this longing for an hour's rest to distract your every waking moment!

—Hasn't the spirit of man supremacy over the body? As long as my spirit lacks anchorage I am as worthless to life as life is to me. The best I can do is to seek until I have found.

—Did your spirit find rest there?

—No.

—What did you find?

—That the quietness and peace of the place only deepened my own longing and increased my restlessness; that I could not join in the singing of their hymns without being dishonest; that their god is not mine—and never can be; that their religion is the same I rejected long ago; that I hate myself for the duplicity in my makeup; that I am more lonely than ever.

—How long have you known that?

—Instinctively since my first visit.

—Why do you go?

—I am so alone.

—More alone than other lonely ones?

—N-o-o-o, but weaker.

—How do you know?

—Well, I go.

—That proves nothing. When did you try not to go?

—Never.

—Why do you go?

—Mercy! Thousands upon thousands go. Their lives flow on like a placid stream. They neither doubt nor believe. They are not aflame for truth. They don't lie—openly. They succeed in their endeavors. They don't suffer excruciatingly. They are not capable of feeling deeply. They pray luke-

warm prayers to a lukewarm god, who gives lukewarm happiness to their lukewarm days. I hate that!

—Why do you go?

—In the eyes of a few I saw a light that fascinated. Their
personalities spoke of a power that had lifted them above
mediocrity.

—Is that what you sought?

—I always sought the highest.

—Always?

—Yes, always.

—What is "the highest"?

—That which is sanctioned by the god within.

—Does he sanction your churchgoing?

—It seems not.

—Then you no longer seek the highest?

—I don't always have the strength.

—Does he condone your weakness?

—No.

—Then you don't always seek the highest?

—I am human.

—Does he contend that being human is a barrier for
reaching the highest?

—Man is a product of his environment.

—Who is he then, "the god within"?

—Who am I?

—A product of your environment, you just stated.

—A human being is one who has a god within.

—Then does it not follow that being human is no barrier
for reaching the highest?

—Man is a dual being. There is a constant struggle between the god within, and that which is a product of environment.

—In other words, a struggle between the lowest and the

highest. But if you defend your lowest actions, you have forfeited the right to call yourself a seeker of the highest.

—I don't defend my actions. They are a fact, I admit. I sought truth even in church. I seek it everywhere. But perhaps more than truth I seek power—power to live—meaning in life. I thought I might find it there.

—You thought?

—I hoped.

May 27

THE WORLD—without God—is a desolate void. The more you listen to the god within the stronger grows your longing for contact with SOMETHING, SOMEONE—THE GOD WITHOUT. Your life lacks meaning and your work a final goal if HE is not. You want to die. You haven't strength to win.

May 28

BOUNDLESS ENERGY is like a ferment within. Longing to do is like a fever in my blood. I must get free from this dependency. But how? Nothing seems worth the effort until this is clear: Does God exist? And what is my relationship to HIM?

—That is a question.

—But am I justified in giving it so much of my time? Can the answer be found by my mind?

—No.

—What can I do?

—Work.

—Study?

—Abandon yourself to a great cause.

—What cause is great that does not have God for its goal?

—Proceed from the assumption that it does. Work as if you stood before God, and your faith will produce Him.

—If my faith produced Him, He would not be a reality, independent of me.

70

—No reality exists independent of everything else. Philosophy has taught you that. God is God to you first when your innermost being opens itself to Him, just as light becomes a reality to you only when the retina of your eye receives it.

—I can't accept that. There MUST be SOMETHING that is absolute!

May 29

MY REASON, Thought, or whatever you are, tormenting, dissecting, analyzing, I hate you!

—I am you.

—No! I am tremulous, longing for peace and rest, for eternal arms to embrace me, for understanding beyond all limits. I am a human being with an insatiable hunger for happiness. But you! You are doubts that kill, truth that wounds. You have a whip in your hand and you strike without mercy. You dissolve longing into its components to prove that it is not idealistic. You distill emotion to find its sediment. You dissect with your cold steel the vibrating nerve of a mood. You analyze every expression of the soul under your merciless microscope. You make me a herbarium. I hate you.

—I am you.

—If you are I, then I will kill that part of me which is you.

—That is to be a Christian.

—Is that why I can't?

—That's why.

—I hate you, yet I won't kill you. A word from the Bible comes to me, "He that loveth his life shall lose it, and he that hateth his life in this world shall keep it unto life eternal." Those words set organ music vibrating within. How unutterably solemn everything becomes!

—I AM completely alone.

—You have me.

71

—Who are you?

—Your Reason.

—That rebukes and scourges.

—That helps you to get above your confusion of mind and feeling.

—That would exist at the expense of my feelings. Something must be sacrificed. Would I become a Christian I must deny you. Would I follow you I must disregard my feelings.

—The question is: What is primary and what is secondary?

—What is?

—Ask the god within.

June 1

I CAN'T PASS by a church without feeling a stab of pain as if reminded that a dear face has forever vanished—a fond hope has forever been crushed and the door of home forever shut by alien hands.

—Oversensitive fool! Get hold of yourself! Be rational! Work!

—I am unfit for life.

—Become fit!

—Where can I get the power?

—Don't ask for it. Work!

—Why should I work?

—To be fit for living.

—A life without meaning?

—You are a fool.

—I am what I am. What made me such?

—A product of—

—Stop it, Scourger! I can't take it!

—Then time has come to bow down to the god of Christ. He desires those who are nothing in themselves. Before

Him you need not stand courageous and strong. I, your Reason, will no longer torment you. He will lead you on beaten paths, and I will be subservient to Him. A peace that passeth all understanding shall be yours. You need no longer thirst for truth, because He is—to you—truth. To follow Him will suffice. Your days will flow on as the wavelets of a placid river. And no more than they will you fear to lose your way. He carries you. And everything that comes your way is sent by Him. Every church will be a home to you where your devotion will find Him. Its sacred melodies will gently cradle you to dreams of everlasting bliss. Prayer will lift you above all irritation, all obstacles. You need no longer forgive yourself or suffer over your failures. He will forgive you.

—Voice of my Reason, I will not silence you! My limitation is your bondage. When you speak in irony and sarcasm you feel the pressure of your chains, and struggle to get free. Strike, then! Torture, dissect and scoff. Your freedom shall be my strength. I will follow you.

—To follow me is to sacrifice.

—I am willing to sacrifice.

—To follow me is to suffer.

—I am willing to suffer.

—To follow me is to be alone.

—I am willing—

—Don't lie.

—I won't lie.

June 5

Who are you that weeps and weeps within me? Why don't you speak? Why don't you cry out your woe? Why don't you leave me in peace?

73

How far run our trails together?
Who offers a friendly hand?
Here everyone is so lonely
Far, far in alien land.

Fellow humans, is this life? Is it reality or masquerade? Do you all have a face behind the mask? A face contorted in pain and longing? Eyes where hunger for freedom burns like a flame? Hands seeking, seeking? Why do not our hands meet? Why don't we snatch the masks away? Why don't we mingle our tears and love each other, we who are under the same condemnation?

June 25

SERENITY, a quietness of mind is enveloping my soul. The struggle is no longer bitter. I am reading Marcus Aurelius' *The Communings with Himself* as I go to and from work. They inspire to humility and honesty above all. They teach me how transitory everything is, and of how little importance man is, how soon he is gone. "All the things of the body are as a river, and the things of the soul as a dream and a vapor; and life is a warfare and a pilgrim's sojourn." They also show me of how little consequence is age. The septuagenarian in dying loses as much as the lad, for neither possessed more than the present moment, and you can't lose what you don't have. I was rather startled to find that Marcus Aurelius also speaks of "the very deity enthroned in thee." "Let the god that is in thee," he says, "be lord of a living creature that is manly, and of full age." He speaks of "dignity without affectation, an intuitive consideration for friends, a toleration of the unlearned and the unreasoning.— To be at the same time utterly impervious to all passions and full of natural affection. To praise without noisy obtrusiveness, - - to possess great learning but make no parade of it." I like this emperor-philosopher. "This that I am," he

74

says, "whatever it be, is mere flesh and a little breath and the ruling Reason."

June 30

To GIVE UP a cause when it becomes difficult, when the contrary winds are stronger than anticipated, is not unusual. Most men do. To hang on, grit your teeth and say, "I will!" calls for unusual strength. Not many can—or dare.

July 18

I NO LONGER attend the meetings of the labor union of which I am a member. It's hopeless. Clique-leaders manage everything to suit themselves. For that matter they are practically always in the majority. The actual majority of workers never attend. They pay their dues and remain passive. And why should they go and listen to some meaningless wrangling?

A few have urged me to lead an opposition in an idealistic direction. To that I don't feel "called." I lack objectivity as well as competence. I hate strife and division. There exists an organization that in my opinion works in the right direction. I have repeatedly attempted to interest our union in an alliance, but in vain. That's as far as I can go. The union movement is not the highest, and I must not consciously give myself to anything less. The labor movement is greater. It includes the union movement and goes beyond it, but even that is not the highest. America has not progressed beyond the "union" idea, which is not surprising in a land where the golden calf is so openly worshipped. I am not sure I have more sympathy for the self-complacent bricklayer in his Overland than for the blasé capitalist in his Packard. Both live only for themselves.

Possibly I am biased in this. Could it not be that with a social system like America's, the labor movement had to take its present course? The "defense" had to be geared to the methods of "the enemy" in order to survive. And "the defense" as well as "the enemy" are only two factors succeeding one another in the unfolding of tomorrow's Utopia? Therefore when the private capitalist, driven by his fever for gold, his ambition for gain and fame, through lucky speculations, aided by trusts and monopolies, extends his power until the shining steel of the steam engine crisscrosses the globe, gigantic ships plow the seven seas, the mountains yield their ore, the earth its marrow, its oil, its coal, and millions get their substance out of his hand, he himself is only a tool in the hands of progress and his motives are only means to a greater goal than he ever dreamt. Through him must come the epoch of industry and invention. And when his contribution is accomplished, the legions of the proletariat come marching onward, making of his creations common wealth for the masses. And so when little Mrs. Morris, in our union meeting, opposes every effort except the economical, she too, unbeknown to herself, is a tool in a never relaxing evolution. Then "gross materialism" is not a boil, a defect, a chance occurrence, but an essential link in the chain of progress. The individual vanishes. Generations, world movements, and epochs become steps, transitional periods. "The world cause," says Marcus Aurelius, "is a torrent. It sweeps everything along." And behind this dizzying gigantic plan there is no "thought," because thought presupposes a THINKER! Driven by blind laws, this world system moves ever onward, over graves and crushed hearts of little humans!

August 10

THE WORLD WAR excluded everything else on our program tonight. The monstrous, incredible thing has happened. It was a relief to be with these Russian Jews, who feel passionately and express themselves without restraint.

The fact of war is enough to make one lose his mind. It's a slap in the face of every intelligent being. It's the declaration of the bankruptcy of our civilization.

I am glad father is dead. He who always said that war in our times is unthinkable. I am glad for all that are dead. One is ashamed to be alive, to be a participant of this horror.

A world immersed in blood and tears because the philosophy of lunatics has been tolerated.

Or can it be that even behind this there is a reason—a purpose? If generation after generation of men give their lives in the forward march of culture, what then is the significance of a few millions giving their lives in *one* generation, if through their dying Utopia is brought nearer? It's the reasoning of insanity, but who can think sanely tonight?

September 5

I HAVE SCRAPED together enough to take a course at The School of Civics and Philanthropy. I must find a field of labor so humanitarian that my own little bit will be a direct contribution towards the development and liberation of the Race. I hope that social service will offer me this opportunity. The labor union movement has lost its halo. The cause of the laborer was to me sacred. It was the cause of freedom. The liberation of the laborer was synonomous with the liberation of the race. Organization was the method. During the hectic days of the strike, how earnestly I labored to get a true perspective and convince myself—and others—that the method was justifiable. It involved sacrifice, but the price of every forward step had always spelled sacrifice. The liberation of the race could only be bought at the expense of the individual. How many saw this? It was this question that crippled my enthusiasm. The individual cried for more bread, light, happiness—for himself. This end seemingly justified all means. Is egoism, then, the driv-

77

ing force of progress? Is the laborer's egoism more just than the capitalist's? Yes, I replied, because it includes a greater good for the many. But did the individual choose his station? If suddenly placed in the opposite camp would not the same force—egoism—serve as conveniently there? Does it follow then that the cause sanctifies the means? "Cause" and "sanctify" are two ideas that introduce something higher beyond the struggle. But for both parties, end and means are one. On the one hand, greed of gain was the driving force. On the other hand, personal profit was the aim. Could this ever become SOMETHING HIGHER?

What then is my egoism? A higher standard for the many? They cry for more bread, light, and joy because that is their present need. When they have it, will they then begin to hunger for the things I hunger for—beauty, knowledge, truth? And when our goal is reached, if indeed it is, will we not find that all we have gained is a new set of needs? Fulfillment, then, is not the answer but rather the struggle to attain. A melancholy outlook! No wonder the old philosophers wept! I feel like weeping too. I am the product of the suffering and sacrifice of generations past. And I must suffer, sacrifice, and die to bring the race one little grain of dust nearer a goal I do not know.

If this is the meaning of "social service" let me consider the cost and my own resources. First and last there must be ceaseless service, a constant self-denial. Then, flowing into my own life are all the misery and ills of humanity, its suffering and shame, its crime and sorrow, its degradation and poverty. Through it all I must keep my heart tender, ever warm and filled with understanding and sympathy, never allowing it to become so used to the ills of humankind that it does not instantly respond. In a word, I must live every moment an energy-consuming life with no known source of power to draw from. I must choose that which is absolutely the highest—always—and never compromise, but rather increase my demands on myself, knowing no other incentive, no other goal than progress itself. Has anyone strength for that? When the workday has ended for the normal individual, he hastens home to waiting loved ones. Chubby little arms reach up to embrace him, tender words caress his soul, and the hardships of the day find their meaning and reward in contentment and rest. But when the workday of my life has ended, I stand on the last span of an unfinished bridge and gaze into the pitch-black night of nothingness, conscious that this I, encompassing everything that in the realm of matter never could be explained, now is to be dissolved into atoms, and its lifework become a grain of sand in the cementing of tomorrow's Babel. And this thought is to inspire me to accomplish the impossible!

But in my reasoning all roads lead to Rome. It doesn't matter from what point I proceed, forever I arrive at the same question: What is the ultimate meaning of life? When I now enter into a new phase of life, I am not so much conscious of a negative experience in my past as I am of a radiant hope that sometimes borders on certitude that a positive Reality not only exists but will some day be revealed to me.

September 10

Is IT NOT TRUE for all of us that we seldom live in the present moment? We all look forward to tomorrow. Tomorrow's interest is life itself. If tomorrow has no interest, it is dead, and I don't want to live it. And we are never sufficient to ourselves. Like the snail, leaving the shelter of his shell, we extend our feelers outward, gropingly, longing to touch something, someone, at the same time fearing that this new something might be a danger. But rather than crawling back into my shell, I risk the danger and seek the pain.

"Whosoever will save his life shall lose it" (The Bible).
"To be oneself is: to slay oneself" (Ibsen in Peer Gynt).
"To slay oneself is to live" (Froding).

"You forget yourself in the dedication to a great task. Radiant joy becomes the keynote" (a friend).

My evening prayer would be: "Make my will strong and pure, and my thought free. Let me find the pathway that leads to peace and harmony with myself and all who are good."

September 12

AUTUMN LEAVES fluttering in the breeze, yellow and faded, rusty and dry, heaped in the gutters, rustling under my feet, I wish I could die with you and be bread for to-morrow's life.

It is difficult to be a human.

One of my schoolmates was buried today. Happy, a thousandfold happy she! Oh, that it had been I! But no! I must fight on, even if the struggle seems hopeless. To give up is cowardly! One of my teachers once said, "No one has entered life without a purpose, and no one has a right to go without a summons." They are words with a compelling ring. Not to will to live is to commit suicide.

September 14

IS IT TRUE, I wonder, as someone has said, that he who has had a glimpse through the portals of philosophy's domains never can forget what met his eye, but must forever return to its alpine air and its sweeping grandeur? And no matter how tired he gets of its loneliness and its icy silence, he cannot shut the door and take the step that leads into the rest and self-abnegation of the Christian faith? On the other hand, is it possible for one who has come in contact with a great, creative Christ-like character to completely free himself from such an influence, so that he does not often feel that he has missed life's deepest meaning because he failed to follow Him Who of Himself said, "I am the way, the truth, and the life"?

This is the crossroads to which I return again and again, driven either by fear or weariness. How awful it would be to discover at the eventide of one's life that one has missed the road.

What is the innermost desire of my heart? To create joy? With that as my goal, how can I hesitate? There can be no doubt about where the greatest joy is to be found. Then there must be something else my heart is seeking.

I know very little, but have great ideas of my own worth.

September 15

THERE is no conflict of duties. A duty is rendered null when another greater duty appears. Is duty hard? Are dutiful people hard, cold? Nonsense! Duty is necessity or the method by which a strong personality masters himself and rises above circumstances, making necessity his servant.

September 16

IT IS NO disgrace to have failed when you have done your best, is it?

September 25

MARIA PALOVSKY is married. I just came from the wedding. It was the strangest affair I ever attended. I was the only Gentile present. How absurd it seemed to me! Only the consciousness that Maria and David had the fullest confidence in my understanding enabled me to maintain my dignity throughout the ceremony. All the while I wondered how these two, seemingly so unconventional, could meekly submit to such antics. A factor stronger than their own conviction guided them: love for David's old parents. I believe I love them more than ever after this display of loyalty and devotion.

The last act of the ceremony was the kissing. Bride and groom kissed not only one another but every single guest, young and old, and all the guests kissed one another. Petrified with dread, I stood in the doorway between the two rooms, fearing that this cordiality would extend also to me! But when I found myself completely left out, the sigh that escaped my lips expressed not only relief but also a queer little feeling of loneliness and isolation.

October 15

THE WEEK is almost over. I have done everything I purposed to do—and more. I sat up past midnight to help another in her struggle. I haven't consciously done anything contrary to reason or conscience, and yet what have I accomplished? Wearing myself out, commanding myself, in order to drive loneliness out—that I can do, but it is not the same as being free. Can it ever lead to freedom?

All my careful attempts to help the other without personal interference only led to a negative result. She gave up. All around me people give up.

October 15

EVERY DAY I meet people whose lives are more interesting and gripping than any book I ever read. Take Fania S. today. She has finished her medical training, but can't find a job and is too poor to open her own practice. It is like peeping out through a shuttered window at pulsing, beckoning life, knowing you can't be a part of it, because you have no clothes.

How can you help anyone as proud as she—without offending?

Tonight I feel rebellious against our social order, our

system, and the rich. I could go down to the corner and preach revolution from a soapbox. Progress is so slow that it seems like stagnation.

November 5

PASSED a Swedish church tonight. It was lit up, and I went in. For several months I have not been inside a church.

This is what took place at the close of the service, when I was on my way out:

"Do you belong to the Lord?"

"Sorry, I can't answer that question."

"But isn't it the most important of all questions?"

"I beg you, leave me alone."

"Why?"

"I can't answer you."

"Oh, you are in a terrible way! You are turning your back to the truth."

"Your opinion, not mine."

"What then is yours?"

"I have told you I want to keep it to myself."

"No friend of Christ would do that. Oh, you are His enemy! It is terrible to see a young person so corrupt!"

I smiled. A crowd of curious, startled people pressed close. I wanted to leave, but three "black-coats" assailed me.

"A child of disobedience! It's quite apparent! Sarcastic, shallow and worldly."—"Indifferent to Heaven and salvation."—"Given to frivolity and pleasure."—"Oh, God have mercy on her poor soul!"

Sentence prayers ascend all around while judgments fall like hailstones, and I stand there, smiling.

"I don't suppose you believe you have any sin?"

"No one is as good as he would—or could be."

"Who then is your saviour?"

"Often I am my own saviour."

"What blasphemy!"

The younger of the three looks at me a little more thoughtfully. Did it occur to him that possibly their tactics were not commendable? He said, "I know it is fashionable these days to doubt and deny."

"Right you are. And what else can a poor little woman do than follow the whim of fashion?" It became increasingly difficult for me to swallow my tears, and I continued, quite earnestly now, "You can pronounce judgment, but to understand and forgive, like your Master, that is beyond you."

"Listen to her! She knows more about the human heart than we do, and still she doesn't know that her own heart is full of sin and self-righteousness."

"Spiritual verities are not measured in years," I said, and left.

Are they praying for me now? Prayer usually improves the praying ones.

November 9

A LITTLE PICTURE CARD from Sweden arrived today, showing a tiny schoolhouse high up in the wild northern wastelands, clothed in winter's robe. In the foreground are a few slender birches, gracefully bent under their burden of snow. Beyond is the lake, with its glistening, soft blanket of white, endless miles of white forests.

How I long for the silence and peace of those white forests! I am sick with longing for a bit of pure snow and nature untouched by civilization. Here everything is unclean, grimy, without beauty.

If only I had a human being to resort to—someone deep enough to drown in!

It is suffocatingly, stiflingly close here! It's an atmosphere that quenches fire and melts snow. I don't want to melt, and

I don't want the flame within to be extinguished! I don't want to become calculating and sensible! Let me be a fool rather than a coward!

November 19

MOTHER! Twenty-five years ago just about this hour of the night you gave birth to me. Would that I could thank you—humbly, simply—for the gift of life! Would that I could believe myself capable of so much good that it would fully compensate you for the pain you suffered!

November 20

MISS C. came in to see me again tonight. Her life and personality I would love to sketch, if my pen had point and softness. What a book that might be! Would it convey sarcasm? Yes, but also softness, because her sharpness is like a protective shell around her vulnerability. I have often seen her on the stairway and in the halls and wondered who she is. One evening she came in to borrow some little thing and stayed for two hours. Since then she often drops in. She is a "spinster" around forty-five. And that's her tragedy. The younger girls in this boarding home poke fun at her. That's easy. Her scorn of modish attire is quite evident. Her coiffeur is as outdated as it is severe, and she is a bit awkward and angular. And then she is German, which is a crime today. Anyone born to such a misfortune ought at least to have tact enough to apologize. But not she.

How it happened I can't say, but suddenly she laid bare her heart.

"I have longed so to be a mother," she blurted, "that I can feel hatred and loathing when I look at little children—other women's children. - - - I was born to be a mother, and I am lopsided, stunted and deformed, because my child was never allowed to be born. - - - The chicken-brained mothers who fancy themselves martyrs! And their sentimen-

85

tal sisters who early and late tell one like me that I have missed the real reason for living. - - - They even dare to intimate that I am selfish, cowardly, fearing the pain! And how they pity me! At least they could keep their pity to themselves. If people are happy, why must they hurt? - - - If they only knew! But they are too narrow-minded to understand. They haven't the faintest idea what an all consuming conviction is. They never could comprehend that there are women in the world whose love for an unborn child is so great that they could never stoop to give him a father to whom he could not look up with pride. - - -"

She broke off suddenly, her face crimson, her lips a tight line. I could think of no adequate words, so I said nothing.

I am sure she wished she had not spoken, and I respect her for not trying to cover up. Poor little woman—and all her poor little sisters! To sympathize with them is to hurt them. Alone and in silence they must bear their sorrow. How dare we ever laugh at the expense of another? Why are we so blind? Here I am, daily brushing against gripping life-dramas, and I am so wrapped up in myself that I, "seeing, do not see, and hearing, do not hear."

One thing is certain: suffering in itself cannot enrich a life if behind the suffering there is no MEANING.

November 25

ALL LEARNED PEOPLE are frightfully fastidious about words. Pity one like me who can feel boredom and amusement over their battles of words. Yet I can think of nothing I desire half as much as to be able to understand and participate.

My next diary I will name "I-ary." What else is it?

November 26

TODAY I spoke disparagingly about another with not the slightest provocation other than the pleasure of talking. She has never hurt me, and the thing I made a remark about was none of my business. It was human? Oh, yes, but contemptibly so. Since when am I measuring myself after the standards of pettiness?

November 28

FOREVER OUTWARD, towards trackless wastes and limitless horizons my pathway must go. Somewhere the alpine peak is to be found from whose crest the WHOLE can be seen, where all the little dividing lines melt together into oneness. But may I never forget that my every day is a part of the Whole—the great Harmony, and that it isn't the work or its character that determines the contours of my life but rather the spirit in which it was performed and the imprint it made on the soul.

December 1

BERGSON's theory of progressive evolution is exceedingly interesting. I haven't had time for more than a superficial perusal as yet, but the idea of Life and Matter as two opposing forces contending for mastery offers a plausible answer to the "why" of multitudinous forms, and the "why" of civilization's many and great relapses into barbarism. I am thankful for the new approach this thought offers.

Is there a link between philosophy and religion? Can I by the processes of reasoning find Him? Or can I know Him only by revelation? By faith's acceptance? Mother used to say, "It can't be explained; it can only be experienced." Is faith experience?

December 12

IT IS AS NATURAL for me to believe in man as it is to doubt his gods.

December 24

HOME, HOME! Oh, to be home! I have never longed more

for a corner that would be mine with the indisputable right of spontaneous, perfect love.

New Year's Night

I AM in the merciless grip of melancholy. If anyone shows me special friendliness I burst into tears.—The last hour of the old year is almost gone. Outside my window a storm is raging. What will the New Year bring? Whatever it is, it must be borne. But I am tired, so tired.

The moments fly. The earth never stops for a thousandth part of a second in its dizzying pace through star-studded space. The clock pursues as ever its monotonous tick-tock. The wind shrieks! A lonely human confides her lonely thoughts to herself while everything moves, although everything *seems* to stand still.

Now the minute hand moves over twelve.

It is New Year!

"Glad and good must man be while he awaits death."

January 25

ON A STAND in Vera's living room there is a little dried-up fern. A year ago it was a thing of beauty, full of luscious, green leaves and curled-up tendrils. Now only brown, broken-off sticks remain of all its glory. I look at it and think, "I am like that. My life is as hopeless as a dried-up tree."

It's not true that I can lift my own soul above the quagmire any more than I lift my body by bootstraps. I can wear myself out, I can command myself. But this does not lead to freedom and growth. Weariness is becoming the dominant factor. It takes stronghold after stronghold from my faith in life. It doesn't inflame like anguish. It isn't poignant like sorrow. It's a creeping paralysis, gradually numbing will, thought, feeling, muscles. Everything becomes negative—a lie. No one is working for another. Everyone is out for himself.

88

After a few hours' refreshing sleep

SLEEP is for weariness what drugs are for toothache. It's a relief—temporarily, but one knows that the next contact will bring it on again. There is another more effective cure for toothache: removing the cause. If putting my finger on the cause for my weariness were a step toward its cure, then there might be hope for me. On the last page of his book, *Progress and Poverty*, Henry George writes, "The problems we have been considering lead to a problem higher and deeper still. Behind the problems of social life lies the problem of individual life." Facing that truth, how could I think of "social service" as a way out? If behind the problem of social life there is a deeper and higher one, then there must also be a point of view so exalted that from its premises I can see THE WHOLE. Until I have found that point of view, I can't determine the relative value of anything. Tolstoy is right, "The best is an enemy of the good." Do not the stars in infinite space have a central point around which they move? Hasn't earth its focus? Can I live without one? Didn't a leading daily remark the other day concerning the suicide of a brilliant, young scientist that he, in spite of his genius and the clarity of his thinking, had never found anchorage? Emerson's words come to mind, "A hero is a man who is immovably centered." Let me still search then for the absolute GOOD as the only possible centrical point, lest I at life's eventide shall find myself like Peer Gynt.

January 30

A BABY BOY has come to Vera's home. He is a bright little thing with long, black hair and jet-black eyes. Nathan is already building pinnacles on the castle of his dreams for this son of his. It is lovely to dream with them. Has their life now found its center? Would it satisfy me?

89

A young medical student, Philip Heines, now lives with them in Maria's old room. His soul is not as trumpet-tongued as the rest, but he has eyes that penetrate closed doors. I enjoy thinking with him. He is honest to the core. His honesty is like the surf breaking over you. It makes you feel clean, invigorated.

February 4

I HOPE I will never get so tired that I lose all hope. Started to read Ibsen's "The Lady from the Sea" tonight, but was too tired to go beyond the first act.

When I was a child, my conscience often troubled me, because I forgot to pray in the morning, but in the evening I was driven by fear of the dark. I am still a child.

February 15

Is MY LIFE going to grow like a river, "richer, fuller, deeper"—or the opposite? Will I be ever hopeful, ever ready to begin anew? Will I ever be ready to follow through—succeed? I am still expecting the tables to turn, still believing that what looked like failure will turn out to be the trial that lifted the struggle to a higher plane. If I am mistaken in this, then I have failed indeed, for I have deceived myself.

February 20

FAR, FAR AWAY into a dim, shadowy distance my Utopia has receded during these years in a world metropolis. Everything depresses me: the glaring contrast between poverty and luxury, the milling, ever surging stream of humanity, the endless facades of sooty skyscrapers and, most of all, the everlasting, ruthless scramble for the dollar. Nothing seems idealistic. Everything is "business." Churches and movies vie with each other in sensational posters. Even medical science stoops to commercialism. Behind a seeming philanthropic cause, gain can be found as the motive power.

90

To illustrate, every week lectures on various subjects are advertised. Who is behind the good cause? The city or state or some cultural organization? Oh, no, a daily newspaper—for advertising purposes. Many city and state officials "buy" themselves into office in order to "make money" during their terms.

I would like to believe that what I have just written is true only with qualifications, but true it is.

Besides, isn't it wrong to criticize something good because the motive behind it was not idealistic? But is it? There is something within me that insists on order and harmony. When as a child I stumbled onto the relativity of everything, it almost broke my heart. Now I am beginning to see in this fact an indication of the logic I crave. If all the values inherent in our moral existence are relative, then there must of necessity be somthing ABSOLUTE as the basis for the evaluation. Is this SOMETHING behind us, so that the perverseness is the result of a departure from its laws, or is it still in the future as something yet undiscovered?

But it was about America I was writing! The difference between America and "the old world" may simply be that America applies consistently and in all its consequences the principle, "look out for number one," which in the old world is tolerated and practiced in secret and on a smaller scale. It follows that there must be a reevaluation of all values. Money is put in the center and recognized. Then there is no shame connected with the bowing down before its altar to worship.

The fact remains that America belongs to the future, and the future to America. It's a land growing in power as well as in population. As a state it doesn't spend vast sums to care for its aged or to alleviate poverty. That is left to the capitalists—or their wives. Hence there is a surplus of charity but a want of justice.

91

February 25

TODAY I was sent out to investigate a case where help had been requested. In a dark basement apartment of a tenement I found a young woman sick in bed and a frightened little girl clinging to her. To my horror, I recognized Miller's wife and child. Immediate help was needed. Clearly, they were both half starved. I glanced around. Poverty leered from every object, every corner. After a few words of explanation, I ran to the store and with the few pennies I had in my purse bought some suitable food and prepared a simple meal. They didn't know me, and I didn't give my name.

Finally, in broken sentences, I got the story. Miller had made some blunder at the factory and had been dismissed. After that he had never remained more than a few days at any job. He had spent on drink not only his earnings but the inheritance from his father and everything of value in their home. In less than a year they had come to this.

I sat there and looked at the wasted, careworn face, and I felt so deeply for her that I couldn't hold back my tears. It was just as well, for when she saw me weep, the tension and anguish lessened in her face. She reached out and took my hand. The little girl put her arms around me. I lifted her up in my lap. Silently we wept together. But that there could be no end to our tears we both knew. I met her glance and saw that she realized it. This sorrow would never end until the power that held Miller was broken. Society might help them get on their feet outwardly. The sick one could be given medical care and food until she was able to help herself. The husband could be forced to work and support his family, but that would not solve the problem. Their happiness was wrecked, their confidence broken, and the root of their tragedy so deep that no mere human power could remove it.

This is the problem that is higher and deeper than the social. If there is no power that can awaken and transform, then the struggle is hopeless.

February 26

WHAT impossible situations pantheism can create!

A classmate invited me to dinner in her sister's home, where she lives. The sister has two perfectly adorable youngsters—a girl of seven with long curls of spun gold, the bluest eyes anyone ever saw, and a complexion so clear that it actually seems to reflect light; and a comical little fellow, two years younger, with hazel eyes, brown hair, and a bewitching smile. For the mother the best description might be "lovely." Everything about her seems perfectly harmonious.

In the midst of the small talk at the dinner table the little boy mentioned God. "God," said sister, knowingly, "is in everything that is beautiful." At that moment fruit was passed around, and in selecting a fine apple she added, "God is in this apple, because it is very beautiful."

"Then," said little brother, "I will eat God."

"Oh, no, you don't," replied sister, "He goes out before you eat him."

It was not possible for me to share the amusement that followed. The little girl looked startled and embarrassed. "Can I eat God, mother?" she asked. The answer was evasive.

Did the episode teach the mother something? Did she realize that the day will come when the child's mind will not be satisfied with a halting reply? Does she not need more herself?

February 27

WHAT I WROTE on September 5 of last year is truer than I knew. All the misery and ills of humanity are daily flowing into my life. Today I came across an old woman, dying in filthy rags, cursing life, men, and the day she was born. A terrible stream of bitterness, hate, curses, and bottomless woe poured from her lips. I sat there, petrified. Then gradually I became conscious of a rising indignation within myself. First of all, I was angry with myself because I had nothing to give her. Then I was angry with her for expecting the impossible. Then my ire was kindled against people who had fanned the sparks of doubt in my soul and against the moral philosophers who sit in their snug dens and theorize while the world perishes.

What could I tell her? What did she care about "liberty, brotherhood, and equality," even if attainable in a near future? She was dying now. With a bitter laugh she said that death was the end, but if not, Hell could be no worse than her life had been.

On my way home I walked down to the lake. For hours I paced back and forth along the water's edge, trying in vain to get hold of myself. A voice from within kept saying over and over, and over again, "Just one step—just one—just one —" And no other voice answered, but it was as if someone had taken my hand and led me home. Now I know that within my own breast dwells an enemy of life.

February 28

It is one o'clock in the morning. I am too wide-awake to sleep, and my suffering is so keen I must give it expression.

Around ten o'clock I came down to Madison and State from an evening lecture. I was alone and, while waiting for a streetcar, I stepped into a doorway and looked up and down the strangely quiet street. Everything seemed so different this time of the day. The streets seemed wider, the buildings taller, and the people were a different type.

94

Suddenly my attention was drawn to a young girl walking slowly down State Street. She was gaudily elegant. Everything about her manner and attire was designed to attract attention. To further heighten the effect she playfully dangled a little silver compact against the metal top of her handbag, as if beating out a tune.

A hot wave of indignation and shame surged through me. I saw a middle-aged man with a horrible smile meet her, turn around and follow her, first a few paces behind, then side by side, when they turned around the corner. Unreasoning anger held me. I felt capable of running after them with a whip. Then I discovered that another had observed the episode—a shabbily dressed woman across the street. Her hollow cheeks were lavishly smeared with make-up. The unkempt hair hung in wisps under a wide-brimmed, faded hat. The high-heeled shoes were badly worn and cracked. The eyes shone with an unnatural, feverish glow. A couple of rogues brushed rudely against her, scoffing and leering. She made a wry face. Then a most terrible fit of coughing seized her. Her whole emaciated little body shook violently, and she had to hold on to the wall to keep from falling.

Impulsively I ran across the street to her side, saying, "You are ill, let me take you home!"

She looked up with deadly fear in her eyes. Then she blurted out angrily, "None of your business. Beat it! I can take care of myself. What do you want? I haven't done anything wrong. You have no right to lock me up again!"

"I don't belong to the police. I am just a girl going to school. Won't you come with me to my room and have a cup of tea?"

"You wouldn't ask me, if you knew."

"Yes, I would. Please come!"

95

On the way home I was the one people looked at. And I didn't care. I felt nothing. It was as if everything had frozen up inside. She said nothing. When we got up to my little room I asked her to take off her coat and hat and sit down in the rocker while I prepared the tea.

The terrible tension in her was visible in her face. The hurt of it seemed unbearable. Out of the corner of my eye I watched her. She glanced around the room almost as if looking for escape. Then her eyes rested on the picture of mother with me, only a few months old, in her lap. Something sentimental within me wanted to pull the picture away and hide it. Then I blushed with shame. Tear after tear rolled down her cheeks, streaking the paint. I didn't ask for her story, but haltingly, now and then interrupted by coughing, she told it.

The sum of the sad tale was that she was an orphan who ran away from the institution where she had been placed. She was only eighteen now, cast out, despised, sick, homeless. Was there no hope for her? Wouldn't she go to a rescue home and begin anew? —Begin anew? Did I know what I was talking about? Hadn't she resolved and promised? But all that meant nothing. There was something within her that drove her out, a hunger and thirst that must be satisfied. No power on earth could set one free from such. Now she was too far gone. No home would take her in. The only thing remaining for her was a certain despised section of the County Hospital. She knew that. The police would take her there some day. That was the fear that lurked in every moment, around every street corner.

"Hope for her?" Had I ever seen a fresh, beautiful rosebud trampled underfoot on a muddy street? Did I believe there existed a process whereby it might be restored to its freshness and beauty? If so, there might be hope for her.

It would be useless to try to describe what I felt. I suffered. It was like standing on the shore and seeing a loved one drowning, with no possibility of helping. Why do I say "loved one"? Well, she suddenly seemed so. An unspeakable tenderness welled up within me—but not just for her. She became the representative of a class, living in a quagmire. In some way I felt responsible that the quagmire existed, but most of all that I didn't know how to help her out of it. Then I thought of Mother. What would she have done? What would she have said? I knew it. Should I try to say it as she would have? I took Mother's Bible.

"Lottie, this book tells about such a process. It is the most wonderful thing that has ever been written. This is what it says, 'Though your sins be as scarlet, they shall be as white as snow; though they be red like crimson, they shall be as wool.'"

She leaned toward me and asked breathlessly, "How?"

(I don't want criticism now. I was not myself. I was Mother.) I slowly turned over the leaves and came to this verse, "I, even I, am he that blotteth out thy transgressions for mine own sake, and will not remember thy sins."

Again she asked breathlessly, "Who?"

As if an unseen hand had led mine, I always found what I sought. "He was wounded for our transgressions, he was bruised for our iniquities; the chastisement of our peace was upon him; and with his stripes we are healed. All we like sheep have gone astray; we have turned every one to his own way; and the Lord hath laid on him the inquity of us all. . . . For God so loved the world, that he gave his only begotten Son, that whosoever believeth on him should not perish, but have everlasting life. . . . I am the bread of life: he that cometh to me shall never hunger; and he that believeth on me shall never thirst. . . . Him that cometh to me I will in no wise cast out. . . . If any man be in Christ Jesus, he

97

is a new creation; old things are passed away; behold, all things are become new."

She drank in every word. She clung to each one as a drowning man might clutch a straw. Then she asked, as intensely as if her salvation might depend on the answer, "Do *you* believe?"

The strain had been terrific. I broke down and wept uncontrollably. She became deathly still with the stillness of hopelessness and despair. "Don't weep! Please, don't weep! You couldn't help it wasn't true. Something so wonderful couldn't be true. But don't weep, don't—"

The sentence was never finished. A spell of coughing seized her. I thought it would never end. Suddenly blood spurted through her lips, and she fainted.

Now she is in the County Hospital. I went with her in the ambulance. I didn't want her to wake up and find the police by her side. She didn't wake up, and I wasn't allowed to stay with her.

I am tired—so tired. For years you can be as young as ever, then suddenly—in a few moments of time—you are old.

Already I can hear the pulsebeats of the new day. How do people carry on?

March 2

A THOUGHT: If a constantly expanding and deepening knowledge of everything's cause and character finally—after millennia of seeking—should lead to the discovery of an absolute intelligence, God, why should it seem unreasonable that the soul in a moment of unclouded vision spans the centuries and in faith embraces the Eternal One when faith becomes the guiding light that sheds radiance over an otherwise weary trek, with goal unknown?

Is it perversion within me that insists that to accept revelation by faith is synonymous with a departure from the world of thought and a shutting in of oneself in a narrow world of mystery and superstition? Or is it sound intelligence that protests against a step in open defiance of reason?

But my reason can't comprehend God. It can't take a step outside its own realm. The step of faith is a leap into the dark unknown. Will I make that leap some day when I have grown too weary chasing mirages in the wastelands of reason to care whether I sink or swim? This is the danger I fear.

If I must make the leap in order to advance, let me make it fully conscious of all that is involved! Would that I could stand, self-contained, on the borderland of reason, after having explored its regions, and say: Within your domain I find nothing that can satisfy my spirit's hunger, or the craving for meaning and order that is inherent in my being; therefore there must be in existence another realm, my native land, and I am now going to find it.

After that I would never attempt to reconcile FAITH or, rather, REVELATION with the so-called findings of science, but instead evaluate those findings by the measuring rod of REVELATION. Could it not be that this is the breeding place of the world's confusion? Man is ever attempting to subordinate a greater to a lesser, and when he fails, he scraps the greater.

It is early morning now; therefore I can think without sentimentality. When evening comes, and the heavy artillery of the day has rumbled through my soul, I can only hide in a corner and weep over the woe of the world.

Evening

No, I can't keep this up. Either I must find something that is unshakable, or I must give up. I have sounded the depths of weariness until I have lost all sense of proportion.

99

On my way home I visited Lottie in the hospital. She lay there with wide open, fever-bright eyes. There was something so helpless and lost, so forlorn and hopeless in her eyes that for a terrible moment my heart was still with unbearable pain. With her face free from makeup and her hair combed straight back, she looked very different. The moment she saw me a glimmer of joy, a shining gladness, flickered over her face. I wanted to embrace and kiss her, but had been warned not even to take her hand.

I love her. It is as if I had known her a long, long time ago and had suddenly found her again. I know it sounds unreasonable, but it is so anyway. She must die soon, and she knows it. She says that it doesn't matter. She has nothing to live for. I know that is so. She has nothing to give to life, and life has nothing to give her. But hot rebellion comes with that thought. I feel that there *must* be hope. Now she clings to me as if I knew all the answers and couldn't go wrong.

A student from a certain Bible institute had been there shortly before I came. She had read some of the passages I had read, and Lottie told her that because I didn't believe them she couldn't. So now it's not only for myself I am responsible but also for Lottie. Possibly for others? This is the great solemnity of living that we either help or mislead others with our lives.

Would that I could believe—for the sake of Lottie! I almost think I am capable of repeating what I did as a college student in Stockholm, when I regularly read the Bible to an old, blind woman and prayed with her as if God were real. But that is out with Lottie. She already knows where I stand.

Sometimes it seems as if faith lived its own independent life within me, as if all I needed to do to reach complete rest and harmony was to take one single step, the step of faith. If I could, without qualification say, "GOD," the step would have been taken. But I can't and be fully honest. If God is, He must give me the faith needed for that step. And still, I often feel as if faith did live within me. It must be so, or I couldn't live.

March 3

RUTH has reached her breaking point. She has brooded, sought and suffered. Today something broke. I knocked at her door this morning to ask if she were ready to go to school with me. As soon as I saw her I knew. Not that I understood, but I knew that she had reached her breaking point. The strange and terrifying thing was that she herself seemed to know it. It was as if she could read my thoughts and speculated how she might hinder me from calling a doctor. Two terrible hours followed. Suddenly she became violent. Then others came. Now she is locked up. She was a gifted soul, high-strung and supersensitive. And she lacked anchorage.

Life is difficult.

March 5

WHAT IS MAN? Like nothing else. Here I go, day after day, feeling the tightening grip of sorrow closing me in, and yet for hours on end I can cut myself free from everythingthing that hurts, and become completely absorbed in a subject, wholly impersonal and abstract. But no matter how impersonal it may seem to begin with, it ever leads to a problem that, as far as I am concerned, lies in life's centrum.

Of late I have studied Russian literature. It is the subject I drew for the essay I am to give before the Jewish-Russian Club. What if my observations are secondhand, borrowed from others, who in turn borrowed them from still others! How could I—after only a few weeks of study—

give anything original or independent? But if I could help my friends to glimpse something of the beauty and truth my own eyes have seen, it would be well worth our while.

The older writers move me deeply. I am limiting myself to a few of them. I shun—shall I say with greater truthfulness?—I fear the younger writers.

A few weeks ago Maria gave me a new Russian novel that soiled my soul. In blank, unguarded moments pictures from that book flash through my mind and make me feel that the evil depicted is part of me. Am I more immoral than most?. Do I respond more quickly to sensuality than most? That is something I can not myself determine. But I know that many times I have wished that I had never read that book. If sensuality is something that awakens sensuality, and if it is something that degrades the soul, why should it be foisted upon the world under the label of literature?

In my work I come in daily contact with the victims of sensuality. Their heartrending misery and hopeless despair ever call forth scalding tears. My compassion for them grows with my hatred of this monstrous evil that has ruined them. There are times when the fanatic within me would break forth and cry aloud against a "morality" that ever balances on the borderline of the forbidden. Could I but work my hands bloody tearing down all the billboards of despicable movie advertising that line our streets, it might calm my soul. But you don't do things like that, if you value your liberty.

But these "new" books do not affect me that way. They attract and intrigue with their artistry. I go to them with soul receptive and eager, as in childhood I went to the great classics. Slowly, drop by drop, the poison begins its deadly work. Before I know how it happens, I am living in a world against which—under normal conditions—I would instantly have rebelled. It is one thing to speak the truth; it is another thing altogether—cloaked in a mantle of truth —to revel in sensuality. The cardinal sin of these books is their trickery. They glamorize filth until it loses its identity. Perversion is realism. This must have happened to our critics. How else could our book markets be flooded with filth?

It seems to me that Ruth voiced a truth today when I visited her in the hospital. On her face was the great calm of resignation, as if she had been given a glimpse behind the curtain of the incidentals of time, and viewed the harmony of eternal verities. She said, "I have looked and listened since I came here, and I have wondered why these people are here. I prefer to stay with them. They are normal. The others—outside—are insane."

To defile or murder souls is certainly as insane or criminal as to attack bodies! I feel the deepest sympathy for "Slatte" (I believe it was "Slatte") in Rydberg's *The Gunsmith*, who hung a man because he was profane.

Am I an old-fashioned, narrow-minded fool, adhering to archaic laws and therefore not a part of today? At twenty-five, am I becoming a prude? Something within me proudly replies: "I don't care!" What I know, I know, and what my conscience dictates, I will speak. Let men call me what they please! How my conscience came to be, I don't know. How much guilt another bears in his own shame, I don't know. (It is true that often when I view the circumstances in the life of a fellow being, I feel that everything can be explained and forgiven.) But this I know—whether or not there is a God without—within me there is One whose impelling voice I cannot ignore. The chapter dealing with His origin is a different matter and of less practical value than the fact, learned by experience, that implicit obedience to His dictates leads to harmony. If I could cease from living while I seek the answers to life's great problems, perhaps I could afford to ignore or deny the laws of my conscience, but since I must constantly live so intimately near to others that my every word and act reflects on their well-being, and since I can't get away from my own dual personality (a body governed by appetites and a soul filled with yearnings), I must follow this mystic voice that never yet led me astray.

There are spiritual people, and there are materialistic ones. I prefer the spiritual. And I prefer a book that "rings the rising bell in the dormitory of my soul" rather than one that stimulates my animal instincts.

March 7

IT IS LATE night—or rather "the wee hours of the morning." Again I have been lost in Russian literature. I have been reading Brandes, Kropotkin and Phelps. The latter, a literary critic, calls Russian and American literature twins, but with a vast contrast, partly caused by the difference in the age of the two nations. In the early years of the nineteenth century, he says, American literature sounds like a child, learning to talk and aping its elders, while Russian literature has the voice of a giant, waking from a long sleep and becoming articulate. "It is as though the world had watched this giant's deep slumber for a long time, wondering what he would say, when he awakened. And what he has said has been well worth the thousand years of waiting."

Realism and a shocking honesty are characteristic. "A Russian novelist, with a pen in his hand, is the most truthful being on earth." Frankly Tolstoy tells what he is, that he loves honor and fame so much that if presented with the alternative he would choose that rather than goodness.

And when he wrote that, he was already well on the way to world fame. Humility and honesty go hand in hand. Compromise is unknown. If he is orthodox, he is blindly so. If a free thinker, he becomes a nihilist. If a believer in the idea of authority he bows his forehead in the dust before it. On the other hand, if he hates it, hate will press the bombs of revolution into his hands. He is radical in everything. And underneath all there is melancholy.

Quietly, the peasant in the Gorky novel asks: "What does the word LIFE means to us? A feast? No. A battle? Oh, no!! For us LIFE is something merely tiresome, dull—a kind of heavy burden. In carrying it we sigh with weariness and complain of its weight. Do we really love LIFE? Love of Life! The very word sounds strange to our ears. We love only our dreams of the future—and this love is Platonic with no hope of fruition."

According to Phelps, suffering is the cornerstone of Russian life and fiction, but the immediate result of this suffering is sympathy and love, promising much for the future.

This critic seems to be deeply religious. He quotes Gogol, who says that the greatest value of the Russian nature "consists in this, that it is capable, more than any other, of receiving the noble word of the Gospel, which leads man to perfection." He adds that all the world's philosophy and wisdom never have improved on the teaching of Christ, and that "what the individual and society need today is not Socialism, Communism, or Nihilism; no temporary palliative sought in political, social or financial reform. What we each need is a close personal contact with the simple truth of the New Testament."

It seems in whatever direction I turn I must face this. Tolstoy, Gogol, Dostoevsky, Henry George—all end up here.

105

March 8

FINALLY—white snow!! This is what I have longed for. It snowed all night and nearly all day. For a few fleeting hours soot and dirt are hidden. All is white. But people are quite helpless. Traffic is almost at a standstill. It is interesting to note how emergencies and extraordinary situations bring out the best in people. They are drawn together, forgetting—or paying no heed to—conventionalities. What if all of us could live a life of constant newness! How beautiful life would be! We would smile at each other and exchange happy words, as today. We would help each other to make living a gladness.

There is a Bible word that speaks even of this. Something about the inward man being renewed day by day. Strange, how the Bible ever seems to have an answer to life's deepest problems!

March 10

GOD IS! It sings within me and reverberates in a thousand echoes, GOD IS! Life's central point has been found. There is an ultimate, absolute FOUNDATION, resting on itself alone. This certitude has given wings to my feet. As with a stroke of magic it has transfigured life.

How did it happen? How can one for seven long years go blindly stumbling in the dark and then suddenly see?

"The gift of God is eternal life." This is the only answer.

Tired after the day's work, I wandered toward the lakeshore. My steps were as heavy as my thoughts. As so often before, I stopped to admire the new church on the boulevard. It is finished now, at least on the outside. I obeyed a sudden impulse to enter the courtyard and rest a few moments on the snow-covered rim of the fountain. It was very quiet in there; there was hardly a sound. Through the row of pillars in the graceful colonnade I could glimpse the lights from cars speeding by, but no pedestrians could be seen. It was as if life itself had halted in its irresistible flight to give a little human being repose to find herself—and God.

There I stood, drinking in a sermon of harmony from pure Gothic lines. My soul seemed to expand. It was like standing on the summit of a mighty mountain. Everything small disappeared, even my weariness. Awesome wonder filled me, and deep within me I heard great organ music. Worshipfully I thought of the mind of man, capable of creating a thing of beauty like that temple. My eyes followed the outlines of the slender spire and lifted to an infinite, star-studded heaven.

Never have stars twinkled more brightly for a child of earth than they did for me tonight. Everything I have ever read about them suddenly came to life. I saw measureless distances and faraway shining suns and planets whirling in ordered orbits in infinite space. I stood in fancy on the glittering bridge of the Milky Way looking down on the infinitesimal speck of the universe, where I spend my little life. I saw myself filled with reverential awe before the product of man's mind and hand, while my eye was too dim, my soul too small to comprehend a CREATION of which man himself is only a part. As in a blinding flash, I suddenly saw THE WHOLE. My mind staggered. The immensity was beyond me. The light was too great.

No, I can't put this into words. I blush to think of my folly in worshiping the created and denying the CREATOR.

I sank down on my knees in the snow, and the deepest thing within cried, "GOD!" And everything without, as within, answered "GOD!" In a flood of tears that knew no bitter surge I was coming HOME.

Now I know faith has all this time lived within me. The last seven years are a bad dream. I am awake. It is light.

GOD IS. Life, I no longer fear you. Your riddles are not unsolvable; your suffering not meaningless; your struggles not hopeless. GOD IS!

March 20

IT WASN'T weariness that reigned today. Never have I been poorer from a financial point of view. I have scarcely enough money to satisfy my hunger, and my clothes are worn threadbare. My shoes have holes right through the soles. But I am walking with my head lifted in eager expectancy of something wonderful I know is coming. The moment I was sure of God a secret spring appeared in my innermost being. It keeps me from painful contact with everything hurtful and harsh. There is HOPE, because there is GOD. A new compassion has been born within for my fellow beings. It is full of tenderness. I want to take them in my arms and carry them HOME. They are lost in the dark as I was.

What then do I know about HOME? Nothing. But I know that HOME is a reality. And I know the meaning of the word.

March 27

"WHAT HAS HAPPENED?" asked Lottie when I visited her. "You look so happy."

"I have found GOD."

Silently, questioningly she looked at me. I told her everything. She was still silent, but her eyes were full of tears.

"Aren't you glad, Lottie, that HE is?"

"Y-e-s, but—"

"What?"

Hesitantly she asked, "Do you believe He is the One who said those things about being forgiven and—and—you know—like snow—and—everything new?"

"I have wondered about that myself. You see, finding Him brought a joy so great that there has hardly been room for questions. I have been satisfied with the knowledge that He is. God cannot be anything but GOOD, do anything but GOOD. We have nothing to fear but all to gain with Him."

"Even when we have sinned as deeply as I have?"

"Ah, you are no worse than the rest of us. You can't help that your life has been so difficult."

"I don't feel that way. When you spoke about the stars, how they shone and led you to Him, I too saw Him, but He was so bright, so great, so far, far away from me that I didn't dare to look. I felt my terrible sin, and that I never could come near Him, and it hurt more than before—unless —"

"Unless what?"

"Unless that book, the things you read, are from Him."

"Perhaps it is, Lottie."

"There is such a longing within me. Everything is so changed. Before, all I wanted was enjoyment and escape, something to satisfy my thirst—the thirst of my body. Now it is as if my body had died and only my mind lives. It never lived before. Now it is thirsty. The things you read made me feel so strange. My hate died. Hurts from others seemed small, while my own guilt grew.

"When I discovered that you didn't believe that One existed who could—and would—take all my guilt, I wanted to forget it all, but I couldn't. At least, Esther, you have given me faith. You did something for me that couldn't possibly profit you or any selfish interest. Then you taught me that there is GOOD. And when you refused to tell a lie even to help a dying girl then you convinced me that TRUTH is.

"It has taken me a long time to see this. I am not used

to thinking things through, but now I begin to understand myself. I wish you would tell me something—just anything you know—about Him who calls Himself 'The Bread of Life.' You are not sure that what the book tells of Him is altogether true, but neither are you sure that it is not, otherwise you would never have read it at all. You are too honest for that. Please, tell me about Him."

"Have you never heard about Christ?"

"No, nothing definite, really. I have heard His name quite often in oaths and once in a while in a street meeting as I have passed by, but I never gave it a thought. It was something that didn't concern me. Now I feel that somehow it deeply concerns me."

So I told her all I could remember of His life from the Gospels, but she led me on with questions so that even the story of creation, the Fall, and Israel and the prophecies came out. Finally, after a long silence, she looked at me and asked with deadly seriousness, "Why don't you believe this?"

And this is the question I now must honestly answer. I was relieved from the responsibility of an immediate answer because a nurse appeared and reminded me that visiting hours were over. I only had time to say that I once had believed but that the thoughts of men had led me to doubt.

Here I stand, still on the summit of a mountain. It is the highest I have ever scaled. On three sides the outlook is free, the horizon unlimited, cloudless, serene. But in the fourth direction I see a mountain peak mightier than them all. Would I reach its cloud-capped summit I must again descend. Down is up. There is no other alternative. My goal is still—THE HIGHEST. And the watchword is still "ONWARD." And the visions on the summit are indeed worthless if they cannot give inspiration, courage, and hope on the tortuous trail.

April 1

SPRING HAS COME. The last snow slush has been washed away in the gutters. The swelling buds of the lilac have shed their brown jackets and are weaving their Easter finery. The lawns in the park are turning green. Spring is everywhere. Winter is gone.

I recall a fantasy from childhood. I imagined that during the winter months all of nature shut itself in to think, and when spring came its thoughts found expression in new leaves and flowers. Now there has come to me a new sanctity, embracing all of life. I see in every new leaf and flower an expression of God's thoughts. Even the stars are His thoughts of light. And people, not as they seem to be, but as they ought to be, are His thoughts of love. His thoughts always become realities, facts, deeds. They spring from immutable certainty and grow into something positive. They never fumble in the dark as do mine. Would my thinking arrive, reach its anchorage, it must be akin to His—be His thought in me. And would I accomplish something with my life, then I must find myself as I sprang forth in His intention.

"For it is God which worketh in you both to will and to do of his good pleasure." So writes Paul. To whom does he write it? The Christian. But not all Christians. On Sundays I have seen a deacon in a big church who has a very sanctimonious mien, and he assists at the Communion table. But he is the owner of three tenements of the lowest type, with primitive plumbing and stinking sewerage, broken windowpanes stuffed with rags, roofs leaking and every vestige of comfort lacking. Here hundreds of human be-

111

ings drag through a weary existence and have to pay outrageous prices for rent. Is that "Christian"?

Another "pillar" in another big church runs a factory that employs scores of girls that are paid such starvation wages that many of them "sell" themselves to live. Is that "Christian"?

A woman I know prays weepingly at the weekly prayer meeting for "the heathen," while a few steps from her own door there lives a widow (with six small children) who never can get away to hear a sermon, and that woman has never even called to offer assistance.

No, I see it clearly, it must be with a real "Christian" as it is with God. His thoughts must become deeds. He can't think nobly and act badly, because the act is the fruition of the thought. Therefore if his deeds are not good, he can't be a "Christian," a God-man.

So I have come then to identify a God-man with a Christian! What is the next step? To identify Christ with God?

April 2

LOTTIE'S QUESTION is still unanswered. Now I must call on her again. What can I say? She has awakened in a world where everything is simple — a child's world. Thought complexes do not exist for her. There is only a simple "why" and "therefore." Perhaps the simplicity is largely due to the fact that she is close to the borderline of eternity. Were I in her position, fully conscious that my next step would take me to the threshold of death, perhaps even my voluminous problems and overgrown emotions might shrink.

It is useless to go back, to try to figure out how doubt began. The question is in the present tense, "Why don't you believe?" I must begin anew, and I must begin with Him who truly is the center of the question.

112

April 4

BURNED the midnight oil last night reading through the Gospel of Matthew in English. It seemed as if I had never read it before. Expressions of transcendent beauty and pungent truth thrilled and gripped me. I was brought face to face with the rejected King of the Jews, and I fail to understand why they rejected Him. Neither can I understand how anyone could interpret the Sermon on the Mount apart from its connection. Where can one find a human or a group of humans who in their own power could create a society where these "laws" were kept?

How does one become "poor in the spirit"? "Poor," someone has said, "does not imply the want of possessions but rather the possession of a great want." If my spiritual poverty overwhelms me, it can only be because I have met ONE whose spiritual wealth knows no limit. And if I am to "hunger and thirst after righteousness" it means that I must have seen my own guilt—and that of all the world—in the light of absolute righteousness. And how do I become meek and humble? How do I get the heart that suffers, sorrows, and rejoices with another as if the sorrow, suffering, and joy were my own? If such life-giving streams can issue forth from my innermost being, then I myself must be in contact with "THE ABSOLUTE." But it is not so. My every impulse for GOOD is a reflection from an ideal I have seen—without—and in my heart embraced. But the ideal I see in the Sermon on the Mount is so stupendous in its demand that it would drive me to despair unless—it is difficult to form that word—unless that contact is possible which alone can lead those streams from the heart of God through my own.

113

April 5

NEVER let me forget that my own religious scruples to others must appear imaginary and petty.

If only I could find the chain of thought whose logic leads, link by link, to a certainty beyond doubt.

April 6

WORK and responsibilities abound. I am never lazy. Even when most lonely and tired, I work. Why should I not give myself that recognition when it is true? An inward peace has been mine for a long time, and my faith in God has grown day by day, for every day brought an answer to prayer. In the evening I have asked, "God, grant me a work to do that is big and difficult and give me understanding and humility to receive strength from Thee. Let me never rest in mediocrity and small attainments. Let my hands ever reach out for the impossible and my eyes ever seek limitless horizons. Thou art my God and Thy greatness is beyond comparison." And the size of the task and its performance was ever conditioned on my soul's receptiveness to power from above.

I am proud to be a human being consciously striving for perfection.

April 7

I REFUSE to believe that the thousands upon thousands who today are jobless, breadless, and homeless are personally responsible for their plight. Guilt? Yes, but not individual, rather collective.

"For I the Lord thy God am a jealous God, visiting the iniquity of the fathers upon the children unto the third and fourth generation." Why should this be interpreted as malicious vengeance on the part of God, when science has demonstrated the existence of a law of heredity? Is it as the Creator of natural law that we criticize Him? Such

114

utter childishness! Does not every law of our physical universe give irrefutable evidence of balance and harmony? Only when the law is broken does disharmony ensue.

But if the individual is not accountable—or only partly accountable, does it not follow that God is impersonal—at least in proportion to man's unaccountability?

April 8

GRETA WRITES that her sister has been ill ever since the baby came, and adds that marriage frightens because of the great physical and spiritual sacrifices it entails. It would be interesting to hear Miss C's comment on that. How she would deride and scorn! Even I feel cynical. Such superficial nonsense! The union between man and woman—in love—is natural and HOME—with all it entails of pain as well as pleasure, of self-effacement as well as self-fulfillment—is the indisputable birthright of LOVE and the CHILD. A normal woman should not under normal conditions "suffer" but grow through motherhood. Is it strange that society is warped with such individuals? Or are they a product of civilization? What a tribute this! Evolution ending in confusion.

In most instances individuals could—were they only big enough—create more reasonable conditions by refusing to submit themselves to the unreasonable. But how are they going to get big enough?

April 9

I NEED to get more large-hearted and realize that my relationship to man can become an avenue to God even as it is a result of my relationship to Him.

Forever I am meeting myself anew and forever discovering new doors, entering new rooms, and forever I must make new decisions.

115

April 10

SPENT THE NIGHT with Maria. It might be egotism leading me there. They esteem me so highly.

David is a realist—or rather a materialist. When he puts forth his reasons and conclusions I sit there thinking, "Oh yes, it sounds logical, but I am too tired to build my life on it." But my lips remain silent. Am I a coward?

April 11

IF A DUTY meets me that I refuse to accept because it seems to impede my own progress, where is the guarantee that the performing of that duty was not the door to new conquests?

A schoolmate of mine was rebellious because she was called home to mother her dead sister's babies. But she went. That SEEMS of primary importance, but is it? *How* she went is the essential thing.

April 12

THE CLATTER, rush and crush of the city torture me beyond words. It is like living on a gigantic stage where everyone is wearing some sort of disguise, playing some role. Hardly anyone seems at home with himself, and rarely can one find a soul that doesn't accept the play-acting as reality.

How I long for spontaneity and truth, for greatness in simplicity and simplicity in greatness, for souls that choose to wear their own threadbare garments rather than borrowed finery!

April 13

PRAYER is not—should not be—a momentary attitude but a state of unbroken rest. If my soul is at home in God how can I fear?

Father, the road is dark and rough, but You are near.

116

Did You not give me to life? How then could the streams of life through me be retarded? Must they not because of me flow on and out to others, glorifying You?

April 14

I AM FREE only to the extent my will is merged in God's.

April 15

IT MUST BE quite late. My watch has stopped. Around nine o'clock I began reading Ibsen's *A Doll House*. It held me spellbound until the last curtain fell. A masterpiece that—a bit of life itself. I love the drama more than any other form of literature. It doesn't merely narrate. It lives. The work of the master is ever drama, ever acting, portraying, self-luminous, moving. Look at Strindberg. He doesn't speak about his *Archipelago Types*. They speak.

April 16

I HAVE ever looked upon myself as a seeker and thinker, basing doubts and convictions on facts. Lately I have seen how often I was mistaken. Since I began to read the Bible daily and become acquainted with its language, the religion of Christ is opening to me unsuspected depths of meaning. A single sentence—a word even—can, like a sudden flash of lightning, reveal vistas and horizons I never dreamed existed. And ever clearer I see how little I know.

But if this new knowledge does not help me to live a fuller life, to give more love and understanding, if it doesn't double my patience and increase my fortitude, it is useless —or I am.

April 17

IT WAS pure gladness to wake up this morning, as if I had won a great victory over self, or as if the day before me would bring some unspeakable joy, or as if the hand of God had led me safely over an abyss.

I used to wonder why I should strive for victory over self when indulgence didn't actually hurt either myself or others. That may be logic, but it's negative. What *good* have I accomplished by not indulging in anything directly evil? The idea of *good* is positive. You can't term a sleeper good because he is not doing anything bad. Would I commend myself on the sleeper's "goodness"?

The deeply rewarding joy of overcoming is a hidden secret to him who has never experienced it. What fathomless depths, what expanding horizons of meaning life has in store for the spiritual!

Father, I thank You for the day now passed and for the rest awaiting. My soul longs for You. You are the wellspring of light. Could its streams flow unhindered through me, then even my little life might give a faint reflection of Your glory.

To that end lead me!

May 10

ONLY THE LONELY submit their thoughts to paper. Two are silent.

On the 18th of April it was my turn to read my paper on "Russian Literature." All I am conscious of from that night is a pair of black, penetrating eyes, ever seeking mine, and when my own were held captive by them, it was as if we two were alone in all the world. We have been alone ever since. I have seen more of him than of anyone else these past weeks. And he is infinitely dear.

There never was a spring like this. Never was life fuller, richer, more beautiful. There is an unspeakable exultation within. I can hardly contain myself. Should this continue —or my joy increase—I just couldn't bear it. Something would have to break.

Happiness has come to others, and I could understand

118

that, because the lives of others were like books I have read. Everything is possible in books. But that happiness like this should come to me, Esther Winge, that is incomprehensible. A rich, wonderful soul has met mine, opened itself to me, and with love embraced me.

God is infinitely good.

May 11

LIFE is an unspeakable gift. My gratitude is beyond utterance. I kneel down by my cot in the stillness of the night when my happiness is too great for sleep to thank the Eternal One, but my joy is like a turbulent river, drowning the words.

May 12

How I used to long among friends for the silence of understanding, the opening of one soul for another so completely that motives and desires could be read before they were clothed in the concealing mantle of words.

It has taken me a long time, my Father, to learn that You alone can thus decipher the script of my soul. I thank You that in love You have now revealed it to me. Let me never forget!

My own love I place in Your strong hands. Mine are not strong enough to hold so precious a gift. Give me only enough each day so that no one may need to leave my door empty-handed.

Sometimes it seems as if my love for him and my faith in You are one.

This I know: my life must be a divine service.

May 13

FATHER, make my life to be an overcoming, convincing life. Let it be characterized by dedicated sincerity, vibrant love. And let it be uncompromisingly Yours! Help me to attempt even the impossible and from You expect the perfect. Your holiness demands perfection. Let perfection then be my goal.

It is easy to be gentle and good when your tomorrow is so full of hope. You feel, somehow, indebted to all mankind.

May 20

LOTTIE has gone HOME. Yes, that is what it was—a HOMEGOING. I stood by her bedside and saw her go. Phil, too, was there. He is now an intern at the hospital. He learned to know her story through me, and she learned our secret. From that day she withdrew herself even from me. I sometimes wondered if she didn't feel some bitterness over all she had suffered and missed and because no hope remained for her. But now I am ashamed of that thought. She really had been liberated from every earthly attachment. She had begun a new life in a new world. Our happiness never made her jealous. She just looked at us from the vantage point of her new world and prayed that we might not become sufficient in ourselves.

Her question—why I did not believe—she never repeated, and I never offered an explanation. I did attempt to show her that every individual must for himself believe—or reject—and personally bear the consequences. I gave her a copy of the Gospel of John, and as long as her frail hands could hold the little book she kept on reading it—over and over. Through that book she seemed to become a stranger to us—and we to her. She was always shy with Phil, perhaps because he is a doctor, perhaps for other reasons, and since he so often came when I was there, Lottie and I seldom had a chance for a longer conversation. Actually, I do believe, he came to spare me from such conversations, and she seemed to sense that too. But even if she gave

120

very few direct expressions of her faith, she gave to all that came near her an undeniable, unmistakable evidence of the power of the Gospel to transform life and impart joy.

Perhaps no one else saw the transformation more clearly than I, and to me it is a fact more binding than any so-called axiom of logic. It also imposes on me a moral obligation that staggers me. And that it should stagger me brings surprise and sadness. Should I not be glad and thankful that I have such evidence? Am I then discovering something within me that doesn't want TRUTH at any cost? Is it cowardliness? Do I fear men? Fear to be considered narrow? Or is it Phil? Is it some threat to love's fulfillment I fear?

Nazarene, your way is the way of the Cross. Over it lingers the shadows of Gethsemane and Golgotha. It is a negative road. I can't believe it is the way of LIFE and TRUTH. You must have been mistaken. Your followers are simple-minded and foolish. They don't amount to much. Their lives are not convincing, their thoughts not free. I can't accept - - - -

And yet, there is Lottie!

Ah, you poor, despised little outcast! The night I found you, had I honestly analyzed my feelings, I would have had to admit, my impulsive action and aching pity notwithstanding, that I was infinitely far above you, and now the roles are reversed. You are the accuser. The rose that had been trampled in the mud by cruel, unheeding feet was restored to its pristine beauty. So free and glad and radiant your soul became that in its flight it cast a gleam of glory on the discarded garment you left behind. And here I stand, ready to deny that fact.

I believe, then, only what I want to believe?

Esther Winge, the trail you face leads down. It is steep and slippery with very little support for leaning, and the

121

shadows are lengthening. In one direction there is light. There beckons all you have secretly longed for—a home, a sheltered nook, indisputably yours with love's prerogative, and by the side of the beloved a great task, noble, dedicated, recognized by the best. In the other direction the shadows deepen, but there I see SOMEONE with hand beckoning. Is it Lottie? No, ONE infinitely more commanding. Why, oh, why must I make the choice? Or must I? Isn't my imagination running wild? Can the thought suggestion of another reach my mind causing me to see shape and substance in shadows? If so, can my own mind trick me to believe that which I most desire in order to justify my choice?

It is time to meet Phil.

C—,Michigan, July 23

MY PHIL, if you were here, my happiness would be complete. Perhaps I could then forget that out there in the wide world unrest, strife, and bloodshed still rule, that men hate and murder each other. Here all is serene. One day is like another, and over them all the sun shines: sun over glittering waves, sun over the snow-white locks of an old man, and sun in the heart of a little woman.

Mostly I spend my time with the old man down on the dock. He seems lost in his own thoughts while I dream about you and our future. We sat thus last night at sunset. My hands lay idle in my lap while his were busy mending a net. For him all labor seems rest, and nothing can be more restful than to see him work. He is the first human being I have ever seen who always seems to be at home with himself. For a long time I sat there looking at his rather stooped form, the fine, old head with its flowing beard and wise eyes. Behind it I saw that of another, young, dark, strong, arrogant, and it belongs to me with

122

love's royal right. I found myself longing for the many days and the hot pursuits through which you and I shall walk together toward the cool repose of sunset.

Suddenly the wise, old eyes lifted and met mine. They were so full of understanding and goodness that they held mine captive, while I felt color flooding my face. He resumed his work as if nothing had happened, but now I know he knows our secret and I can talk with him about you.

God bless you, darling!

The 28th

MY DEAR! It was only yesterday you were here and yet I am waiting for you. All my soul cries out for you. You must sense my longing in your dreams and in solitary moments.

Tonight I sat a long while on the bench where we rested after our long hike. Everything was so still. It seemed my longing alone had life, but after I had listened a long, long time to its heartbeats, it merged into oneness with all nature. Everything waited with me for the sound of your footsteps. The broad, silvery way of the moon over the waves became the royal road of my love to you, Softly a gentle breeze touched the top of the tall trees and the leaves whispered, "Is he coming? Is he coming?" And the breeze answered, "He is. He is." The birds twittered, "He is dear, dear; he is dear." And the waves murmured, "He is near. He is near." Everything is holding its breath waiting for the first sounds of your steps.

But you are in the heart of the throbbing, noisy city, and the moans of pain and fear are ever in your ears, night and day. Aching limbs wait for you and tired eyes look for you. Your presence and help is their only hope.

In thought I follow you on your rounds. There are several I can't get out of my mind. Old Susie in 72 is one of them. As long as I live, I think I shall remember that face with a hole where the nose should have been. And little Mary in 43, paralyzed for seven years. And Kirchner in 42, his whole body contracted by pain. I am glad you are there to bring them some help, but mostly I am glad because it is given me to come into your life and help you to help them. If I didn't already know that God is, I would understand it now. There just *must* be *Someone* to say THANK YOU to for a gift like that.

Vera and Maria had a hot argument with our hermit about spiritual things. They are incorrigible realists, and he opposes them frankly—and loves them dearly. To me he said, later, "They are like the scent of pine woods to dust-filled lungs."

August 3

No, PHIL, I can't yet answer the question in your last letter. I know you have been waiting, but I just can't. To you it is so simple. Your parent's religion—as far as you are concerned—is only an old quaint fairy tale. Nothing more. Because your love and respect for them is so great, you keep this fact from them. A "Jewish wedding" would lead them to believe that I shared your pseudo-faith.

You say the whole thing actually has no significance, that our love alone is important, and that because it is so great we can afford to make this concession to another great love. From your point of view, which is that of the agnostic, that is true. But Phil, I am not an agnostic. Have I given you occasion to believe that I am? I am sorry. You see, I haven't as yet come to a clear understanding of what I believe. I KNOW that God is, but I am no nearer to Him today than I was that night I suddenly "saw" Him. That

124

He *is* sufficed me. Then you came. Since then you have been the center of my whole existence.

I have never known if the bedrock under my feet was my consciousness of Him or of your love. My faith and my love were one. To work by your side to ease suffering and distress, to bring about more humane conditions, cleaner and saner politics and international good will was a gift more beautiful than my fondest dream. That there could ever be a conflict between my heart and conscience was unthinkable. Then came your question. It awakened me. And my soul is a battleground.

Once—long ago—I faced a decision and I compromised with my conscience for the sake of expediency. I have never recovered from the shame. It must not happen again. In our relationship everything must be founded on truth.

Please, do not ask me to answer until I am ready.

Maria's brother is now at the front, and on the opposite side your cousins are fighting. Perhaps they will meet. Perhaps one will fall by the hand of the other! This is insufferable, preposterous! When shall men wake up from this awful nightmare?

Strong, tender words clamor to be spoken, but I hold them back. You know how dear you are to me.

August 11

MY BELOVED, the many operations and pressing duties that prevented you from taking the first available train to me were higher duties. How often I have heard you say that personal interests are secondary. It's not just theory with you. It's dominant conviction. It was this bedrock conviction that first drew me to you. That and your refreshing honesty. Because of this, your conviction and honesty, I dare to expect understanding for my own growing conviction and struggle for honesty.

You say that "no petty scruples, no traditional fables must stand in the way of our happiness." Oh, Phil, how priceless your love; how it fills me with gratitude! Hours after your letter came I would heed no other voice than love's sweet song. With your own words, "Nothing but our love is of any consequence," I silenced every doubt. Over and over again I read your letter. Gradually it dawned on me that it was your unswerving faithfulness to conviction that prevented our being together and that it must ever be so. Our deep inner togetherness and our mutual understanding will make up for that I told myself. It is the unshakable foundation of our happiness.

"Togetherness?"

Oh, Phil, how can I express in clumsy, unwieldy words the crisis that finally crystallized my conviction?

The pain of bringing your parents what to them would appear as the greatest of sorrows will not come through me but possibly an even greater.

You concede—at least indirectly—that your parents' religious belief is to them the greatest, most sacred reality. Your veneration for their belief is my guarantee that you will also respect mine. But when my soul reaches upward in adoration you are not with me. I shall always be conscious that the deepest experience my soul can know is termed superstition by you. On this point "the rock-foundation of our happiness" is insecure.

Through the open window I can hear Vera cooing and babbling with her baby. After a while he will be big enough to learn his evening prayer, but it is doubtful that he ever will. Vera and Nathan agree in condemning that practice. What if it were our son? Because your love is so great you would allow me to follow my conviction even in this. But on this point also the rock-foundation wavers and the suffering for both of us is inescapable.

126

objective: a society built on righteousness. But the means? Your way leads outward. Your code of ethics is a social Then there is our lifework. We agree on the ultimate morality. To you Christ is nothing more than a social reformer, and everyone that fights for universal brotherhood, for a richer life for the masses and for the breaking down of international and racial barriers is to you a "Christian," while you are ready to say with Liebknecht that Christianity is a religion of capitalism and the upper classes. But ever clearer I see that my way leads inward. While I grant you that a Christian must fight for social righteousness, I am nevertheless of the opinion that no one becomes a Christian through this endeavor. What right do we have to misrepresent the teachings of Christ by putting a different meaning into the name? As far as I can see His teaching is primarily concerned with the relationship of the individual to God, and an outgrowth of a right relationship to God the Father is to follow the brotherhood of men. The laws governing His kingdom are found in the Sermon on the Mount, but they are all deeply individual. They bring to mind the words of Spencer in *My Political View at Sixty*, "No new order of society can transform the world unless behind it stand transformed individuals."

I don't call myself a Christian—not yet, but my contact with men and my knowledge of myself have taught me that man does not have the power to save himself, and that without the emancipation of the soul all other "freedom" is a parody. Therefore I am convinced that the prerequisite for a new order of society is new individuals.

So far my conviction is clear and strong. But I can hear you say in your own direct manner, "How are you going to save individuals on such a scale that through them this new kingdom is established since after an experimental period of two thousand years this method has proven itself a failure?"

My answer is: I don't know. But is it not true that your social ethics has had just as long a trial period? We must not make the mistake of blaming the teachings of Christ for the failure of nominal and pseudo Christianity. An aggressor state is not Christian no matter how many or high its temple spires. A clergyman who invokes the wrath of God upon the heads of "the enemy" is not a Christian, nor he who offers up prayers for victory for the armed forces of his own aggressor nation. A Christian is one in whom the Spirit of Christ lives.

What if that Spirit had reigned in all the leading nations now engaged in this most awful of all wars!

What if the great money trusts and monopolies suddenly would be under the sway of that Spirit!

What if politics would be permeated with His ethics!

Dreams, you say. True, but is it not also alleged reality? So highly do men esteem the teachings of Christ that they at any price would claim His name. And under the cloak of that name self-interests run their gamut. Then comes blind, reform enthusiasm, and demanding the abandonment of so deceptive a philosophy. But if a mere nominal adherence to Christianity throughout the centuries has succeeded in molding the contours of national life, what could be more revolutionizing than its essence? It must go with nations as with individuals—all must become new. And because the nation is a composite of individuals, the renewal must take place in the individual before it can be realized in the national life.

How this emancipation is to be accomplished, I don't know. But if it is to be Christian, it seems to me it must be realized as Christ directs.

I have witnessed one such conversion—Lottie's. Any-

128

thing more transforming I can't fathom. Could anyone have been more abandoned, despondent, desolate? And yet her death was like a victor's crowning. In place of fear and unrest, there was joy and peace. Whatever our opinion of the Christian (not pseudo) we must admit that he knows how to die grandly. Look at the martyrs! What freedom from fear! If that old woman who died with a curse on her lips could have found what Lottie had found, would not even her death have been a hymn of praise? And if one knew Lottie's secret would it not be worth a lifelong pilgrimage to bear it from bed to bed of fear-ridden, careworn, hopeless souls? Can't you see that with all our programs and reforms we are powerless to free men from the fear of death or to give them something positive!

I can picture your impatience: we don't live to die. No, but isn't death the last chapter of our living? And in our search for a philosophy that pervades all of life must it not reach that far? And if we find it, is it not a guarantee that it is sufficient to enrich the whole?

There is another evil that no social reform can eliminate. It is that something within man that pulls him down. I know you say that it is not within, that it is education, training—or the want of it, and environment. "Let us improve the race and create a better environment," you say, "and men will become strong, free, and good." Presuming that this is true (which I because of observation doubt) does not our own generation have as much right to happiness as yet unborn generations?

Look at Miller and his wife. They have only one life, and it is shattered beyond repair. If a miracle doesn't happen so that all becomes new to them they must live on memories while the bitterness grows. Where is the "idea" to be found that can awaken Miller and make him a strong, free man who selflessly "offers" himself for a coming generation? No mere "idea" can accomplish that. But if there is a regeneration such as we witnessed in Lottie, not only for the dying but for those in the thick of the conflict, it exists independent of our denial, but assuredly we are the losers.

Phil, my mind has found a starting point which my heart accepts. I am not sure where it will lead, but I have an idea and I want to be free to follow the lead whatever the consequences.

Let us wait a year. It is better to face the crisis now than afterwards. It is better to part in understanding than to be joined together in misunderstanding. Our love is strong, but no love is strong enough to unite souls that never can meet in their HOLY OF HOLIES.

I know this will hurt you, but I don't for a moment doubt your understanding. For us there can be no compromise.

Chicago, August 15

Dr. E. has recommended me as religious director to a girl's reform school in Texas. I was offered the position and have accepted it.

Miss R., the head of the school, is evidently a very modern "reformer." She demands no statement of creed, but wants her girls under the influence of one who is "broad, independent, and sympathetic." I have carefully weighed these qualifications and find that only in a modified sense do they apply to me, but Dr. E. says he will chance it.

August 16

PHIL, I am afraid of you, but still more afraid of myself. Afraid of you, because you make the rock-foundation under my feet to quake. In your arms I no longer know the difference between black and white, truth and falsehood, love and passion. More afraid of myself, because to feel those

130

arms around me I would gladly let the rock-foundation crumble and heaven and earth be lost.

This you must never know, if you don't know it already: I have lost both rudder and anchor. You took them. And now I am adrift. Did you want me so? Is that the way men love?

It is as if I stood by and saw myself drowning. Forgive, beloved, did I not pray for someone to drown in? You are my sea.

The 26th

WHAT IS THIS? Who am I? I am blind and have to be led by the hand of another, and I don't want to see.

If he who leads loses his way I would rather perish with him than reach home alone.

Is this love? Then why am I not happy? Why should I feel wing-clipped, wounded, captive? Must it ever be so?

Either my love is not great enough, or no love—no human love—is great enough to fill the soul. Even in your arms I long. But to give you up!!—NO!

August 27

WHERE is now your conviction, Esther Winge?

It is Philip Heines.

Is that the way women love?

It is the way I love.

Does that mean that now you have found "the highest" to which once you dedicated your life? Or does it mean compromise?

Our love alone has meaning.

August 28

"HOLY PASSION?" Something is amiss, Phil! Those two words—in the sense you are using them—do not belong together. I sense it. "Holy" is a shining word. Let us keep it so. Love in its purest form is holy, Godlike, luminous.

131

It knows no shadow. Purity and goodness are nurtured in its warmth. To love is to sacrifice self that its object may be lifted. Love can never live for itself or, as Peer Gynt puts it, "to itself be enough."

August 29

I AM GLAD I will soon be too far away to see you for a while. This I dare not tell you. There are so many words I never dare to utter, so many thoughts I never dare to think when I am with you. Therefore I am glad to go.

You see, I am not happy. My inner confidence is shaken. Not only am I afraid of myself—and of you, but I am afraid that some day I shall have to stand ashamed before you. You still believe that I am strong and free. When you discover that I am not - - - - - - -

I must become what you think I am.

September 1

GOD INTENDED US for the main thoroughfare, the transcontinental train that never pays heed to flag stops, never stops by small stations, and we lose ourselves on little sidelines and are never on time.

Father, surely Thou knowest that whatever I think, say, or do, the innermost self of me yearns for perfection. Thou art never deceived by the emotional upsets that befuddle my judgment. My pledge to Thee far, far back in the early springtime of my youth still stands. Let me never forget it! Help me to redeem it! Send whatever trial Thou wilt, take whatever joy Thou must, but let me never lose the way! May what is best and strongest in me never have reason to regret!

Cause me to grow strong and good. Allow me never to think petty, unworthy thoughts. Punish me severely for them. Keep me from flirting with sensuality veiled in the garments of hypocrisy. Make me true even when truth

132

makes me unpopular. Teach me to fight for principles—never for selfish gain. Take the dearest of all I possess if it keeps me from seeing Thy thought for me. Keep me as far removed from the insanity of the fanatic as from the limitation of the skeptic.

Lift me to that alpine summit from which I can clearly see life's great realities in their relationship to Thee, and when I have seen them, give me humility and strength to be loyal to that vision, whatever the cost. Give me the perspective of eternity that I may be able to rightly discern the proportionate values of time.

Think Thy thoughts through me!

September 2

OH GOD, unreachably far away are Thy stars. High, oh, so high is Thy heaven. But I thank Thee that it is so.

September 3

JUST FINISHED reading the eleventh chapter of Matthew's Gospel. This verse struck me forcibly, "No one knoweth the Son, save the Father; neither doth any know the Father, save the Son, and he to whomsoever the Son willeth to reveal him." If I now know the Father, that would indicate that Christ has revealed Him to me or else Christ is a deceiver—if not self-deceived. Am I blind that I can't see Him?

September 4

HAVE BEEN READING a lot today. Among many things, two articles on the subject of religion. Both denounce the church. Why do "scientists" and "thinkers" occupy their minds so much with this "problem" when they generally declare that it no longer plays an important part? Do not their acts contradict their words?

I began some thinking on my own, and my thoughts stumbled into familiar paths. This I know: if I would escape agonizing conflicts that destroy my peace of mind, I must faithfully hold on to truth acknowledged by my conscience and experience and not barter that truth for temporary gain. What others think of me is of secondary importance. Whatever sacrifice, trial, separation, or other possible consequences the pathway of conviction brings must ever remain matters of minor importance and never be permitted to influence my decisions. Step by step I must forge ahead, and no step must ever be taken in double-mindedness or doubt.

Paul's definition of sin is undeniably true, "Whatsoever is not of faith is sin." When my soul has lost its confidence, its rest, I have taken the wrong turn and must retract my steps to the exact point where the unrest began. Another criterion of my way of life is its potentiality for joy. Does happiness—deep and real—flourish in its path? Does it multiply and enrich life's values? Is it a royal road on which humanity might reach its highest goal?

Evermore compellingly religion places before me its absolute prerogative. Middle-of-the-road paths were never made for me—nor by me.

Father, let me labor among those who seeing do not see and hearing do not hear but longingly grope for light.

Sunday, September 5

OH, CHRIST, MY LORD AND MY GOD! At last I have met Thee face to face! And all the sin of all my past is as nothing compared to this that I have doubted Thee and withheld from Thee the poor allegiance of my heart!

My kingly Friend, You have stood by my door all these wasted years, and I have not only refused to open but have ignored Your existence. Fathomless mercy, inexhaustible patience! You knew that without You my life would be like a lost hope, an incurable malady, a storm-tossed, rudderless boat, and although I denied You, You stood patiently by, awaiting Your time.

Thou art God, my Creator, the very Source from which Life springs! In Thee I live and move and have my being, and Your hand upholds me as the riverbed upholds the river—and I have denied Thee! Thou art God revealed to men.

MASTER, Thou hast forgiven me. Thou hast bought, conquered, and won me. May all know that Thou art my Master because my life is mastered by Thee!

September 6

HUMANITY's (my) will rising in rebellion against Thy perfect law erected the Cross, and from its suffering there could be no escape until spotless purity offered itself in redeeming love. Thou didst take that place—the only person that could—and with Thy reconciling hand didst bridge the gulf of sin and separation. The moment my hand of faith met Thy outstretched hand of love, a bridge was spanned for my reason over the inpenetrable darkness of life's mysteries. What was once my limitation is now my strength. In the light of Thy love and the holiness of Thy will my every "why" finds its "therefore." In the evolution my faith sees unfolding there is no missing link, and the first does not rest on an enigma nor the last on an assumption.

Now I see how my whole life has been a narrow circuit around my own little self and that I never knew the meaning of progress until I took the step that broke the circle— the step to THE CROSS.

Keep me close to Thy Cross, my Lord, for of all realities it is the greatest.

Morning of September 7

THE NIGHT was spent in prayer—not monologue for God spoke to me more than I to Him. There was far-reaching

135

reckoning, deep contrition, many tears, and unspeakable peace. For such an experience there are no words. Out of a full heart one echoes Paul, "Old things have passed away; behold, all is new."

I am so thankul for all the words of the Bible I memorized as a child. Now they come back to me with new meaning.

Evening of the same day

TRUE IT IS, MASTER, that your way is one of loneliness and suffering. I am beginning to appreciate how You felt when kindred and friends deserted You. Let me not then be numbed with shock when they reject me for Your sake.

Because I am leaving tomorrow I went over to Vera's to say good-bye. Phil was to meet me there, but phoned that he couldn't make it. Maria and David and several of our friends were there. The atmosphere lacked the warmth and freedom of former days. Then someone asked jestingly how I would begin my "reforming" down south. And what religion would I use? An answer in the same vein would undoubtedly have sufficed, but I had no such answer, and when the silence had lasted half a minute everyone knew —as I did—that the answer would have to carry weight. Another half a minute passed. During those moments I caught sight of the Master. Quietly I said, "My conviction is that reform is not enough. I am going to try to introduce to others the greatest of all personalities, Jesus Christ, my Saviour and Lord."

It was like the bursting of a bomb. And the silence that followed was unendurable. I sought the eyes of Maria but, confused, she glanced away. Then in a low, derisive tone David said, "If mother had been here now she would have spit. She always did that when that name was mentioned."

"David!" It came pleadingly from Maria.

136

With a forced laugh someone asked, "When was Esther Winge converted?"

Other voices continued, "Preach to us, Esther, you need not go to Texas to begin."

"Sure, why not convert us!"

"Stop it!" With blushing cheeks and angry eyes Maria sprang to her feet. "Do you think I brought my friend here to be insulted by you? As long as she shared your views you never could find praise enough for her. Then she was farseeing and highminded, far above the average. Then her thought had clarity and her conviction strength. Then she was ever honest and true. Now—oh, you despicable cowards!—I am ashamed of you! Now, when she frankly tells you that her conviction is leading her into a different path, you are so dead to honor and honesty that you mock her. It was the like of you who stood scoffing by the cross of the Nazarene. It was such as you who cried, 'Crucify, crucify!' It was such as you who kindled the flames of the Inquisition. Tolerance! You don't know the meaning of it! You can't stand anyone or anything that differs from your own pet theories. Let Esther Winge believe what she will. To me she will ever be the same Esther Winge, the dearest of friends! Do you hear me? The first one that utters a word against her will never cross my threshold."

It was impossible to remain after that. I mumbled something about meeting Phil and said good-bye. Half numbed and blinded by tears, not fully conscious of what I was doing, I fumbled over my coat and couldn't find the sleeve. Maria came to my rescue. Before, Nathan and David had always vied with one another to assist me. In answer to a reproving look from Maria, David said, "She doesn't need our help. She has Jesus."

＊　　＊　　＊

Master, assuredly Thou art "a man of sorrows and ac-

137

aquainted with grief" and no one can be identified with
Thee without sharing Thy sorrow. Even those who merely
touch Thy life through another become sharers of Thy sorrow. Thou art ever "a stone of offence" and "a stumbling
block," as well as the truest criterion of character. Thy
Cross is the rock around which human thoughts surge, and
every proud crest that does not fall at its foot must break.

A miserable defender I am, Lord! It is easy for me to
become Peter, the denier, or Judas, the betrayer. Make me
at least as loyal to Thee as Maria is to me. Grant, if possible, that these my friends may learn to know Thee, may
meet Thee face to face.

* * *

Phil, what will you say? I know it. Even if all the
world—your world—stood against me, accusing and scornful, you would loyally stand by me and say: "I believe in
you, and you are mine. A world can't take you from me."
You would so speak, because your love is not less than
mine. And so I shall stand by your side until death do us
part. I became your wife when everything within me answered yes to the wordless question of your love. That
promise is binding. The marriage ceremony is only society's stamp of approval, a form we accept in a world of
forms. Whatever suffering we must bring each other, we
belong together.

The crisis has come—and passed. The step of faith has
been taken. It was not—as it seemed—a plunge into abys-
mal uncertainty and mysticism but rather a step into a
FATHER's loving arms. Instead of sinking I found myself
resting securely on THE ROCK OF AGES. Christ won! But
He does not free me from my promise to you. You alone
can do that, and I am not asking to be free. If I could free
you from suffering without sacrificing truth I would not
hesitate, but I see no such possibility. Two alternatives

only are before me: either I take back my promise (and what is that but a slap in the face—yours and that of our love), or I keep my promise, knowing full well the suffering for us both from the things that separate. The question with me is not "Where is the suffering less?" but rather, "Where is the faithfulness greatest?" This, I feel, is what you would expect of me—and what the Master demands.

But you are free. You alone are free. As free as love ever leaves an individual.

I know how you will choose.

September 8

MY GOD, how can this be endured? Will morning ever follow this night?

Phil—Phil—Phil, why did you leave me so?

Sept. 10, on the train

How CLOSELY I clutch my sorrow, as if it were a part of you that still is mine.

That you should go was difficult, but that you left in anger, flouting my love, is unbearable. My pride is wounded, but my heart still more. Wasn't my love the greatest thing I could offer you? The strongest? I never felt it needed an apology. Everything else in me was inferior. I never felt worthy of you and your love. To me it was an unspeakable gift. The greatness of a gift reflects the heart and wealth of the giver rather than the worth of the recipient. I never ceased to marvel over your love. - - -

And you are questioning mine!

* * *

I want to understand you. So intertwined is my life with yours that I have to understand you in order to understand myself.

Your patience was exhausted. Perhaps it lasted longer than anybody else's could have. It must have been difficult for you with your straightforward, practical nature and your clear thinking to bear with my eternal groping and questioning. Was your forbearance anchored in a secret assurance that I as your wife would learn to think as you, see everything from your point of view? Was that why you tolerated my interest in Christ but could not stand my faith's full acceptance of Him?

You are too big to care what others say.

* * *

Then there is the problem of your parents. I mustn't forget them. Veneration for their belief, concern for their happiness must ever be a deciding factor with you. *What* they believe is to you superstition, but that they believe is to you holy. We—the younger generation—are not, in your opinion, entitled to the same consideration, the same right to mold our own lives, and the lives of our own after—what would you call it? I call it the inner experience. (Faith isn't something inherited or transplanted. It is a spiritual certainty as individual as birth.) The only thing you can tolerate in our attitude toward religion is tolerance. A definite tendency—a leaning toward religion—you, and so many of your profession, look upon as a symptom of mental unbalance. With correct treatment, balance can be restored. You believed your love would "restore" me. And so you could not consent to delay. And when I faced you with the confession of this new, deep experience and counted on the understanding I never had doubted, you, who could not acknowledge the reality of that experience, could find no other conclusion than that my love had failed. You were so sure of your own.

I have nothing to forgive you, Phil, and of course you haven't asked forgiveness. You acted as you had to act with the nature that is yours. You could not understand.

140

It wasn't a matter of will—or of goodness. You acted in full accord with your principle of honesty and truth.

And so we had in reality never found each other, and our life together would have been a repetition of my childhood experience, to be hopelessly apart—as one star from another—from the beloved. Nevertheless I am not ready to say that separation is best, because I am not at all sure that the union of souls I have dreamed of is possible. I stand as questioning before love when you leave me as when you came to me. Only this I know with all certainty: you were—and are—infinitely dear. For nothing in this world would I have missed the experience of our love. It is worth even the excruciating pain of separation. I know I grew through that experience, and your going must not embitter or stunt my soul. Even sorrow can be one of God's great gifts.

I never dreamed that you would confront me with a choice. For a while I thought that possibly Another would do that. But I was wrong. At least I didn't see it so. My new life led me out to the positive—toward the fulfilling rather than the breaking of promises. Dear, when you put forth your alternative you didn't know what you were doing. You acted as though you thought that to become a Christian is simply to choose one religion out of many, equally good. It is nothing like that. It is to meet CHRIST, face to face. And to have met HIM is to belong to HIM— or to bid farewell to TRUTH. It is a transaction where the soul stands alone with God and deals with God alone. That transaction is timeless, limitless, eternal. Christ then becomes to the soul what the sun is to its system—the central point around which everything rotates. No one can deny that experience without becoming a traitor to his own soul.

But I can't explain it to you. And you? Could you understand me if you wanted to? Surely, you want to.

141

WHAT A FRIEND WROTE many years ago comes back to me with new meaning: "Through disharmony, despondency, and the abandonment of cherished dreams, the soul is led by the hand of God, as from a cleansing bath, toward the harmony of a new life. When in the crucible of suffering one is able to say, 'Yes,' even if this is taken (the greatest of all I hoped for) I will face it calmly. For to accept all that life brings and transform it into harmonious living is to be truly free."

When she wrote that, she had passed the crisis and "the dearest" had been restored to her. But that is incidental. To be led by God's hand is the secret of cleansing and harmony. To accept the sorrow is victory. If the sorrow is lost all is lost.

When we stand before the searching gaze of the Eternal it matters not so much what we have accomplished, as what we might have done; not so much what we are as what we might have been.

Dear Lord, help me to win the victory whereof the friend speaks! Help me to remember that Calvary's victory was won in Gethsemane!

B——, Texas, September 14

NEW ENVIRONMENT—a new work—a new life. Sun-drenched, windswept, open spaces. Prickly, desert blooms. Little children who early lost their way.

What a blessing to know THE WAY!

There is no room here for tradition or narrowness. My work, as Miss R. expresses it, is an experiment. I must myself "find it."

It is glorious to face a great task, confident that day by day the exhaustless resources of infinite power and love are yours for the taking.

September 16

I AM GLAD that my childhood knew only the light of flickering candles and smoking oil lamps, that the electric light never became a habit. How often I find myself standing with my finger touching the electric button and my mind filled with wonder—as it was the first time—over this marvel. Just a slight touch, and darkness is changed to light! I find an analogy here in the spiritual realm. I am in the midst of pressing duties, wrestling with problems that tax all my powers, or caught in the eddy of unrest and fear, and suddenly, in a moment of inward stillness, my soul is flooded with light, strength, and joy.

I am deeply thankful, too, for the bitter struggle of the past dark years. It has given me a sympathetic understanding for honest doubt that ever seeks an answer.

Let me never forget, Master, that I owe all mankind all that Thou art to me.

September 20

How COMPLETELY mistaken I was in believing that to surrender to Christ is synonomous with intellectual suicide! In Him I became what in no other way was possible—a being in direct contact with the eternal, inexhaustible Source of light, life and truth.

September 21

My MOTHER TONGUE is to me like a caressing lullaby, like mother's gentle voice calling me home from twilight play, like the heart's tenderest melodies, like youth's first bugle call to battle, like that resonant, deep-toned peal of hallowed bells, like the swell of mighty organ music, like the murmuring of woodland brooks and the singing silence of the mountains. My mother tongue is the holiday garb of my thought.

No ONE esteems me half as highly as I esteem myself. And if they knew me half as well as I know myself, they would lower their opinion still more.

When I squarely face that fact, it fills me with wonder that You, who can see beyond the disguise of words into the secrets of thought and will, loved me enough to will Gethsemane and Golgotha.

October 15

THIS THOUGHT gripped and held me today: In a love I can't fathom God sees me, not as I am—tainted and scarred by sin, but as I am in Christ, without spot or fault. Thus I must look at men—through the eyes of love. But I must never forget that the other side of God's nature is holiness. His holiness demands that I become the creature His love sees. Neither can I shut my eyes to the evil I see in men. I must not minimize it or explain it away. I must not spare them the pain that purges.

October 20

MY FATHER! (How near that word brings Thee!) Thou knowest my need. There is no need for me to tell Thee. And in reality that is not what I do when I pray. In communion with Thee I learn what my real need is.

How scornful I used to be with the praying ones. Did they think their God didn't know? Or did they think their own plans better than His? But then I was ignorant of this Father-child relationship. I didn't know that Thou dost reveal Thyself to a soul that draws near in prayer, helping him to glimpse Thy thought and to look at everything from the viewpoint of eternity—until the soul begins to desire what it has glimpsed. That is prayer. Thy answer is ever, "My child, that is just what I most desire to give you." And so that soul grows and becomes intimate with his God, and joyous trust is the keynote of his existence.

May Thy gladness and peace so sing in me today that someone will hear the melody and seek its source. May even the smallest details of my work reflect the radiance of Thy presence because they are done for Thee!

November 1

WHEN I learned to swim, I had to go out beyond my own depth. God's love is a measureless sea. Would I make it my own element, I must surrender completely, yes, lose myself.

It isn't merely that I can't help others when I live in the shallow place, but even God can't help me there.

November 10

Father, help me to help others! I want above all else to be a friend to these girls. In no other way can I help them.

With dislike—if not rebellion—one attends "Chapel" in an institution if the personal touch is missing, if no one there meets one with sympathy and understanding. Rebellion is particularly strong in early youth. How strong it might be in these girls "marked" by society, I may not even guess. If I could only make them realize that their friendship and confidence is the gift I most of all covet! If I could only reach that goal, then my real work would begin.

Meeting with them in classroom or Chapel does not help me much. I am inviting them to an informal get-together in the evening before the ringing of "quiet bell." I have "open house" then in my own room. It has brought me closer to some of them. Anyone may enter without knocking. We usually sit in a circle on the floor and just talk. Sometimes we read aloud, especially in the beginning we did that. Now it is a little easier to get them to talk. But many never come, and many stay away from Chapel as often as they dare. It is to them my heart goes out.

Grace, a little thirteeen-year-old, three times a run-away and twice convicted of theft, came in tonight for the first time. She sat in a corner and listened silently with a half-rebellious, half-hungry look. When the others left, she remained behind. Her thin little hand lay trembling in mine and her great, brown eyes looked almost black in her white, little face. She blurted out in a whisper, "Miss Esther, I hate God!"

"Yes, I know, one can feel that way some time."

"Not you!"

"No, not now, but once I did when I was a little girl."

"And—I—I—thought I—was alone."

"And that is the most difficult part."

"You know that too!"

"Yes, I know that better than anything else."

She put her arms around me and sobbed. I drew her close. When she had quieted down, I said, "Why have you avoided me so long, Grace?" Between sobs she said, "I was afraid. . . . I—hated everybody."

"And here I said to myself, day after day, if Grace only knew how I long for her." She pressed closer.

"It is the same way with God, my dear. What keeps us from accepting His love is only our own mistaken ideas. We think wrongly about Him because we don't know Him. And still He loved us so much that He died for us while we were still hating Him. Whatever the difficult thing is in your life it did not come from Him. He did not prevent it, because He wanted to save you from a still greater evil. Some day He will show you what that evil was, but until then don't you think you can trust the Friend who died for you?"

* * *

146

Master, if I exerted an influence over the lives of others, that—to me—would be cause for anxiety, for I find nothing in myself that is not tinged with weakness. But if Thou, the pure and holy One, so fully controlled me that Thy influence through me might reach others, that would be a never-ending source of joy. I know it is not so. Show me how I am limiting Thee.

November 11

I LOVE—love people. I want to mother them. It hurts me terribly to see them endure suffering they need not endure. If I could only tell them how glorious life is when one walks by the hand of God! No fear, no unrest, no anxious thought. True, the morning's problem may seem impossible of solution, but one does not wear oneself out attempting it, for with confidence and a secret thrill one anticipates the miracle the evening will know. Should the help not come in the manner that would seem most natural, it is because God knows a better way. It is to "rejoice and again rejoice."

"In Thy presence is fullness of joy," sings the Psalmist. One can't draw near to Thee without experiencing gladness —the gladness that comes with the realization that Thou art holding all the seemingly tangled threads of life in Thy strong hand and that Thy love is as infinite as Thy power. This gladness has nothing to do with outward circumstances. It is the light of Thy countenance, reflected in the soul of Thy trusting child.

November 18

I AM never less lonely than when I walk overshadowed by suffering and sorrow, for then I am one with humanity. All do not meet on the sunny planes of happiness but under the dark clouds of adversity. Therefore I thank Thee, my Lord, for the gift of sorrow. It unites me with every-

147

thing living. Because Thou art "a man of sorrows and acquainted with grief," Thou dost belong to all mankind. No one can approach Thee without finding the understanding his heart craves. This is one of the reasons I long to bring men to Thy Cross. It is the focal point of understanding for all the world. But it is more than that. It is the new Mount Nebo from whose summit the soul can catch a glimpse of the Promised Land, and that glimpse more than compensates for a lifelong desert journey.

So glorious is God's thought for man! And through the long millennia He has tried to convey it to us through His seers and prophets, and we have been offended at the garb or genealogy of the Messenger and have lost the Message.

God intended Israel to be a torchbearer to light the way for mankind to the Father's house. And Israel accepted the light as a prize award and separated itself from the rest of the world. And the darkness deepened. But "God so loved . . . that He gave His only begotten Son" - - - "And I," said He, "if I be lifted up . . . will draw all men unto myself."

To truly see the Cross is to be drawn to God. . . . God's thought for "the New Israel"—those drawn by the Cross—is the same as for Israel of old: to light all the world to Him. And the New Israel is like the old. God's thought is too great for them to comprehend. They accept the Cross as a premium and isolate themselves from the world—the world God loved even unto death.

Esther Winge, in your day you are the medium through which God's gift, Jesus Christ, is given to the world. How does that gift look, seen through you?

November 20

REAL SORROW is pure. On its onsweeping tide we are lifted above the commonplace up to the wider horizons of a hallowed experience. It purges the soul and deepens

148

the character. It makes us gentle and compassionate. For when we return from the valley of shadows with an aching void in our hearts, we also carry with us a breath of eternity. and we realize that we are pilgrims only—in a world of illusions, and that we must all go—all separate, and that we must love one another, for time is so fleeting and eternity so long.

My dear friend S. is dead.

November 27

NOTHING has greater attraction for me than to be admired by people who live so close to me that they can see me as I am—without gilding.

November 30

I ONCE heard William Jennings Bryan say that it had given him more genuine joy to lead one soul to Christ than to have been three times nominated to the presidency of the United States. Perhaps it was an oratorial pose by the greatest orator I have ever heard. But I can readily believe him. To see a face suddenly lighted up with the joy and peace only Christ can give is a privilege that far transcends any exaltation or glory the world can bestow.

December 5

As A CHILD I had a great longing to be able to draw and paint. What I saw, felt and wanted to express was clear and strong in my own mind. But I never succeeded. For hours I could be lost in dreams before a bit of white, clean paper and a set of watercolors. I could dream a picture of perfection. But the picture my clumsy fingers drew always brought tears of frustration.

I feel something like that now, dear Lord, every time I try to tell men about Thee. No matter how real Thou art to me, the picture I draw is only a caricature. Teach me,

Lord, so to speak of Thee that men shall see Thee as the reality Thou art and not abstraction or superstition!

December 7

THE DESIRE to write a diary and commune with myself is fast disappearing. When I am alone I seek YOUR company, Master. Every question I must bring to You, and every contact of the day I must discuss with You. When I can look at people from Your point of view I can understand and love them.

December 8

THEY SAY that to believe in Thee is to believe in something contrary to reason, when in reality it is finding the positive answer that eliminates the contradiction. They say that Thy Cross is the epitome of disharmony and darkness, when in truth it is Love's declaration of triumph.

Love is all-embracing. Nothing can be more foreign to its nature than self-seeking and cross-purposes. It has nothing in common with a maundering egotism that indolently dreams itself lifted above the world. THOU didst not die *from* the world but *for* it. A Christ-man must *live* for it.

My Lord, I used to fear the isolation I thought you would bring me. What blindness! How could I forget that You are God's gift to all the world? You do not set me apart from—but rather bind me closer to—life. And life is no longer a dark riddle, a burden to carry, an ordeal to be endured, because beyond it I see the *whole* of which *time* is a part, the very small part my physical eye can see.

Strong, glad, and good must he grow who can glimpse beyond the unrest and dissonance an all-atoning *meaning*. He knows "the peace of God." And "the peace of God" is not only something to die with. It is something to *live* with. And so he that lives in eternity is also living to the full his time-life.

150

True is the saying of one of Your own that he who would be abreast of his day must first be ahead of it, because the present world gets its light from the world to come.

And well I know how unbearable life can be when one can't see beyond the present. No man can chart his course over the ocean of life unless his eyes are on the stars. He that would well accomplish life's mission must live beyond the boundaries of time.

December 12

WE READ an old legend tonight about Abraham. He lived in the midst of people who worshiped many gods, and he earnestly sought one that was worthy of his soul's adoration. Some men worshiped the stars, but when he saw their glory pale and vanish with the coming of dawn he said, "I can not worship a god that fades away." Some bade him worship the moon, but when he saw the moon diminish night after night he said, "A diminishing god is not big enough for my soul's adoration. Then they said, "Worship the majestic noonday sun." And Abraham looked at the sun and found it glorious, but when it gradually sank and disappeared behind the western hills he said, "I will not worship a god that is swallowed up by darkness. I can worship only HIM who made the stars, the moon and the sun, the Eternal, the Unchanging."

Thou, Lord, art the Eternal, the Unchanging. I follow Thee from Bethlehem's manger all the way over Golgotha hill and to Thy empty grave, and I find in Thee nothing that bears the stamp of limitation. How Thy kingliness must have penetrated even the awful garment of humiliation Thou didst bear for my guilt when the thief on that other cross, looking at Thy countenance—marred by suffering, stained with blood, sweat and scoffers' spittle—could cry, "LORD!"

All others had faults. All others failed. Thou didst walk through life—in close contact with men, and no one could find fault in Thee. Thou didst face the greatest crises, the most trying situations, without losing for a single moment Thy kingly bearing. Thou art the Saviour, the Master, the Leader and Guide I need. "Thou hast the words of eternal life!"

Lord, Thou knowest all things; Thou knowest that I love Thee.

December 30

AND so I have found THE HIGHEST to which I early dedicated my life! Tears of unspeakable gratitude and joy fill my eyes, and my heart exults and glows and sings until I can't contain myself. How glad I am that it isn't an ideal—or an idea—my mind must embrace but a living PERSONALITY Who in infinite, eternal love embraces me and all the world.

In vain I tried to join together into coherence and harmony a million broken fragments of life as I saw it. The fragments would never fit. *Then Thou didst come!* And when I gave Thee Thy rightful place every broken fragment fell into place. My outward world took on contour and meaning. Sorrow had its place—and suffering. Disharmony was still apparent, but it became incidental, transitory, the birthpangs of the *enduring*.

In Thee I also found the answer to the enigma of my inner life. In the sanctuary of my soul I traced a pattern that never found its counterpart in the world around me. Its light was never seen on land or sea. The perfection my spirit sought was never found without. The sun itself had spots, and the most exquisite rose had thorns. Even the greatest human I ever met did not measure up to the ideal in my heart. Everything, everywhere bore the mute of melancholy. Nothing satisfied until I met Thee. Thou art supreme. In Thee I find all I sought, knowing full well—with a deep inner knowledge—that in an eternity of eternities I shall never reach a limit in Thee. Looking to Thee, I have learned to know the blessedness of a hunger for righteousness whose satisfaction is in Thee alone. Thou hast taught me that my hunger must grow and grow and grow until it crowds the limitless—and yet in Thee my hunger shall be filled.

Thou art my life—the deep, hidden Wellspring of light, joy and power, the life that makes me feel intimately related to God and anchored in eternity, the life that quickens my pulses and makes my heart sing with joy over the happiness of another, the life that sends words of understanding to my lips and tears of sympathy to my eyes.

Thou art the life I came from, the infinite life awaiting me. Thou art the life I live today with every fiber of my being yearning for the establishment of Thy kingdom on earth. In humble, joyful anticipation I face the greatest of all missions—*to allow Thee to live Thy life through me*. Thou wilt never stand perplexed or helpless before the wretchedness that approaches death with a curse. Thou alone canst give to Miller—and all poor, shackled slaves of evil habits—the power that lifts and frees. In Thy hand shall all the withered, stunted, forsaken, and defiled begin to live "in newness of life." In Thee death has died and life triumphed, for he that believes in Thee—though he were dead—shall live.

"FOR TO ME TO LIVE IS CHRIST."

* * *